POULTRY and
POULTRY-KEEPING

POULTRY and POULTRY-KEEPING

Alice Stern

MEREHURST PRESS
LONDON

Cover photo: Maran Fowl, by John Daniels/Ardea London Ltd

Published 1988 by Merehurst Press
5 Great James Street
London WC1N 3DA

Co-published in Australia and New Zealand by
Child & Associates
5 Skyline Place
Frenchs Forest
NSW 2086
Australia

First published in German in 1986 under the title *Geflügel*.
German edition © 1986 Franckh'sche Verlagshandlung W. Keller &
Co. Kosmos-Verlag, Stuttgart, Federal Republic of Germany

This edition © 1988 Merehurst Limited

ISBN 1 85391 008 2

Drawings by Stephen Dew.
Photographs by Michael Gaisford, Peter Allen and the library of
Poultry World magazine, with five additional pictures from Ardea
London Ltd, on the following pages: 10, 73 (J.B. and S. Bottomley),
78 (John Marchington), 81 (Richard Vaughan), 117 (Tom Willock).

Editor Nancy Duin
Translated by David Kennard in association with First Edition
Consultant Michael Gaisford
Designed by Carole Perks
Typesetting by Maureen Tunningley
Reprographics by Fotographics Ltd, London-Hong Kong
Printed in Portugal by Printer Portuguesa Industria Grafica LDA

CONTENTS

A pair of pure-bred Old English Game chickens with chicks, enjoying a free-range life. The cock bird is light red in colour and the hen is wheaten yellow

INTRODUCTION

Keeping poultry can give a great deal of pleasure, and it does offer an opportunity to 'get back to nature'. However, poultry-keeping has many practical uses, providing eggs, meat, feathers and manure, which these birds produce in large quantities.

While it is true that eggs, poultry meat, eiderdowns and mineral fertilizers are now available at give-away prices, what about content and quality? Who really wants to eat eggs and meat that contain the remains of sedatives (sometimes fed to battery hens to prevent the stress produced when animals are cooped up so closely together) or such drugs as antibiotics, growth-enhancing hormones or the solvent perchlorethylene (found in processed feed)?

Despite ever tighter regulations, the random tests carried out by the authorities cannot adequately protect us from such residues in poultry products. You only have to think of salmonella – which is increasingly becoming a threat to poultry, due to the infrequent changing of the water used in cleaning slaughtered animals, and the inadequate cooking by consumers – in order to lose your appetite for these mass-produced foods.

Nor should we overlook the ethical aspects of mass production, for it is our desire to obtain foodstuffs at ever lower prices which is mostly to blame for the conditions outlined above. When our grandmothers kept poultry, no one asked about the cost/return ratio, and as a result, eggs were extremely expensive. Today's give-away prices can only be offered by producers who keep tens of thousands of birds – at the expense of quality. These birds end up by being nothing more than machines producing eggs and meat.

If, on the other hand, you have free-range products in mind, it should be borne in mind that a free-range hen will require 15-20 sq m (160-210 sq ft) of space, depending on the breed. In order to earn your living from hens, you would need at least 10,000 birds, which would mean 15 ha (37 acres) for the run alone. Since

If you keep chickens you will have fresh and nutritious eggs, and there is always excellent manure for the kitchen garden

For the sale of your eggs, a wide choice of packaging material is available

who has bought this book will already have decided in favour of better quality in his or her diet and will now want to know what is needed to begin.

The most important prerequisites for keeping poultry as a hobby, for partial self-sufficiency or as an additional source of income may be summed up as follows:

- Neighbours who have no objections to this not altogether noiseless form of husbandry.
- A suitable piece of ground – ten hens and a cock will need a run of 150-200 sq m (1600-2100 sq ft).
- Adequate fencing.
- Planning permission, if there are not already buildings that can be converted. In some areas the local authorities impose regulations on keeping any form of livestock in gardens, quite apart from the planning regulations.
- For ducks: a fair-sized pool, and a run of 400 sq m (4280 sq ft) per breeding pair.
- For geese (typically pasture-land creatures): 1500-2000 sq m (16,000-21,000 sq ft) per breeding pair, as well as a bathing area.
- For turkeys: a run of 350 sq m (3750 sq ft) per breeding pair.
- Someone reliable to care for the birds during long absences (with good organization, it should be possible to leave them unattended over, say, weekends).
- If you keep poultry, you will have to be prepared to kill them.
- Patience and love.

only about one third of a bird's food can be obtained naturally in the run, additional feed must also be organic in nature – ideally, home produced.

This means that a truly organically produced egg, from a happy hen, would cost the retail purchaser anything up to three times the supermarket price. Of course, the cost will be less if the buyer goes straight to the producer, but even so, free-range eggs will be more expensive than their mass-produced counterparts.

But enough of complaints. Anyone

Despite, in some cases, thousands of years of domestication, much of the

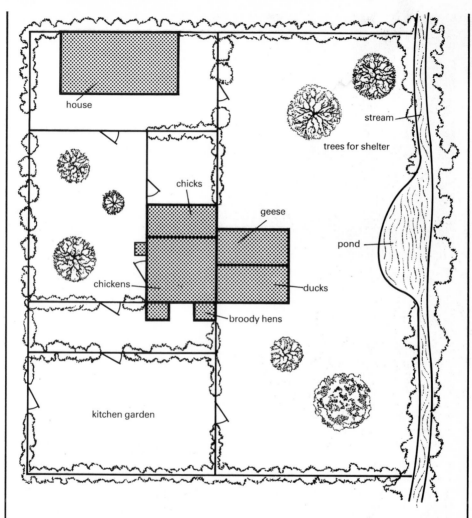

One way to divide up a smallholding for poultry-keeping

behaviour of these birds has remained natural, and all domestic fowl thrive the more their living quarters reflect their original habitat. The more familiar we are with these aspects, the more likely it is that the birds will be healthy and contented.

Thus, we will start each chapter with a look at the various birds' ancestors and their behaviour. The individual chapters build on one another, to avoid repetition. We would therefore advise readers to read the book right through, rather than concentrating on only the birds of particular interest.

CHICKENS

Free-range domestic chickens forage in the manner of their wild ancestors

The ancestors of our domestic chickens can be traced back to Asia – in general, to the jungle fowl of southeast Asia, and in particular, to the small, partridge-coloured Bankiva fowl of India.

As long ago as 3200 BC, chickens were kept as domestic animals in India. However, there are pictorial representations of chickens in Egypt dating back to around 4400 BC. Here, they were initially kept for religious purposes: cocks, with their early-morning crowing, were thought to announce the Sun God.

Later, people came to believe that the behaviour of chickens could foretell the future. Then there was the age of fighting-cocks, and last of all, chickens were kept, first, for their eggs and then for their meat.

During the course of their history, they have spread throughout the whole world, and their domestication has led to many changes in their external appearance: greatly varying weights (dwarf chickens of 0.75 kg [1⅔ lb] and giant chickens of 5.5 kg [over 12 lb]); different coloured feathers (colourings); bare necks; feather-covered legs and feet; crest feathers; minute, multiple and enormous combs; upright and more horizontal postures.

In addition to these factors, their life patterns and behaviour have also undergone changes, but not to the extent that domestic chickens released into the wild would be unable to adapt to their new habitat.

Behaviour of Wild and Domestic Fowl

Compared to domestic fowl, chickens living in the wild are quieter in the sounds they emit, have more ritualized forms of communication, a pronounced flight behaviour when strangers are encountered and a faster learning rate. Bankiva chickens still live in the Indian jungle, or at the edges of savanna woodlands, up to an altitude of 1500 m (4900 ft); like all chickens, they are members of the Galliform family.

Most of their time is spent searching for food, energetically scratching earth from front to back in an alternating sideways direction, using both feet. Vegetable matter, seeds, earth, sand, insects and worms are all swallowed to fill their bodies' own food store, known as the *crop*.

The jungle fowl of South-east Asia – wild ancestor of the domestic chicken

The sense of touch is decisive in this process, for the sense of smell is more perfunctory than developed, and the sense of taste, as with all fowl, is very poor – though wild fowl have a keener sense than domestic fowl. Salty, sweet, sour and bitter tastes are distinguished, but these are only significant when the bird is choosing a food, for if any particular taste is present in any quantity in moist food or water (though not in grain), this can easily lead to the food being rejected.

Pecking

When a chicken wants to peck a grain, it first moves its head far enough back – about 4 cm (1½ in) – so that both eyes can see it. Once the position of the grain has been fixed, the bird thrusts its beak straight at it. If there are more grains close by, the chicken must first raise its head, fix the position of each one and then peck again.

The readiness to peck at a grain depends first of all on its size. The sense of what size is appropriate for a chicken's digestive system is an innate one, but experience, curiosity, hunger or the example of other chickens may result in the pecking of larger sized grains (e.g. maize). On the basis of this experience, chickens will consume larger grains first, perhaps because a faster filling of the crop is an easier way to satisfy the appetite.

Body Temperature

The pineal body in a chicken's brain

For a 'three-dimensional' view chickens have to look first with one eye, then the other

controls its body temperature and its sense of environmental temperature. Normal body temperature lies between 39.8°C and 43.6°C (103.6-110.5°F), being at its highest around 4.00 p.m. and at its lowest around midnight.

Very low environmental temperatures are coped with better than warm temperatures above 28°C (82°F) because birds have no sweat glands. They therefore have to keep their beaks wide open, breathe faster and constantly fill their crops with the coolest water available in order to cool the blood as it flows through the arteries in the neck.

Drinking

When drinking, chickens have to dip their beaks deep into the water, and then lift their heads up high to allow the drops to run down the throat. Chickens prefer to drink with several birds at the same time, all of which conform to the same drinking rhythm.

Vision

Since wild chickens live in forests, their field of vision is limited by the presence of trees and undergrowth. As a result their eyes are focused for small objects up to 5 m (16½ ft) away and up to 50 m (164 ft) for larger objects. Consequently, even today, domestic fowl are not at all happy to move more than 50 m from their housing, which they must always keep within their field of vision.

In order to see things in three dimensions, chickens need to fix an object first with the left eye and then with the right. This is the reason for the typical side-to-side movement of the head and the zigzag changes of direction when they walk; this also affects their balance.

Their sense of colour is well developed. However, darkness restricts their vision considerably.

Habitat and Flying

Following the habitat preferences of their ancestors, chickens shun open spaces, instead seeking out pastures with bushes and similar ground cover as protection from predators and bad weather. When in danger, wild chickens fly to the highest available trees, and even light domestic chickens can clear a 2 m (6½ ft) fence without difficulty, whereas dwarf chickens can fly up to 30 m (about 100 ft) over a building.

For resting at night, wild chickens also settle in trees for protection against predators, in the same way as domestic chickens look for a higher perch.

Sensitivity to Vibrations

A special characteristic of poultry is that they have vibration-sensitive organs: these are distributed all over their skin but in greatest concentration on the legs, and pick up any vibrations from the ground or in the air. This means that the approach of an enemy is detected sooner.

Hearing

Also particularly important for the earliest possible detection of predators in the natural habitat is the sense of hearing. Although chickens, like other birds, have no outer ears, their sense of hearing is very finely developed. The short auditory canal is protected by feathers and a flap of skin.

Vocalization

In conjunction with this highly developed sense of hearing, chickens can produce a great variety of sounds, surpassing almost all other types of bird in this respect. They can make well over 30 vocal sounds, and they begin producing them while still in the egg, 24 hours before hatching.

Chicks cheep with a long-drawn-out, high-pitched sound, and the broody hen replies with a deep, calm 'round' sound – the 'clucking' that gives the name to what are sometimes known as clucking hens. A loud, long, high-pitched falling tone – the cry of abandonment – lets the broody hen know that a chick has lost its way,

The mother hen and chicks use a range of different sounds to communicate with one another

and she answers with a fast, long clucking tone which tells the lost chick in which direction to find her.

Chicks can recognize the 'voice' of their broody hen up to 15-20 m (49-66 ft) away, and the broody hens can, in turn, recognize their chicks at that same distance, even against a background of many other noises.

Chicks will communicate with others in the same clutch by using a soft twittering sound, which indicates a general sense of well-being in the group; they can also produce a warble to indicate danger or fear. However, they do not respond to the cry of abandonment from the other chicks in the clutch.

The broody hen calls the chicks for food by using a short, deep tone. When it is time for sleep, the chicks crawl under the broody hen when she calls them with long, deep tones broken up by high-pitched ones.

From the age of three to four months, cockerels begin to imitate the fighting sounds of adult males; at a later stage, young hens begin to imitate the egg-laying clucking sound. If the young cockerels are without the protection of a broody hen, however, they are so intimidated by the grown-up birds that they do not begin crowing until much later. When they do, it develops slowly from a croak to a proper crowing sound.

Fully grown cocks crow mainly as a sign of their power and for the joy of it. (Fortunately, the most usual time for crowing is not until nine o'clock in the morning!) Lighter breeds have a high-pitched crow, whereas heavier birds have a lower crowing tone which is perhaps easier to put up with. In addition to crowing, cocks also make various sounds to warn their groups of hens (low-pitched threatening sounds) or to call them to a new feeding place (friendly, gentle, high-pitched sounds).

Hens cluck gently to themselves as a sign of well-being, react with a 'gagagi-gagagaa' sound when alarmed, and give the typical cackling sound when laying eggs. Some say that this last sound is made to re-establish contact with the other hens who may have wandered further away. In my view, however, there are two things against this explanation:

1 Domestic hens released into the wild no longer make this cackling sound after laying eggs. They merely join up with the group quietly; otherwise, predators might be attracted to the scene.

2 Domestic hens cluck very loudly after laying eggs even when they are right in the middle of a group of hens. Contact with the group has, therefore, not been lost. A hen's typical behaviour after laying an egg is a proud posture with head held erect, accompanied by loud, self-confident clucking. Perhaps, in the anxiety-free environment enjoyed by domestic fowl in comparison with birds in the wild, hens are overtaken by a sense of satisfaction and relief after the exertions of laying, which dissipates the obvious unrest that can be observed before laying.

Furthermore, wild hens are far less frequently faced with the exertions of

A Silver Laced Wyandotte Bantam cock crows – a small bird with a big voice

High-performance hybrids lay 300 eggs a year – these have the good fortune not to live in battery cages

egg laying: they lay on average only 8-12 eggs annually. Compare this with the high-performance hybrids in modern battery farms which lay on average 300 eggs a year.

For the cock in the wild, clucking before laying signals that he must find a suitable nest for the hen – that is, a convenient hollow in the ground. This, however, is not padded out with lining material; a hen will have to deepen it by scratching the surface. Even the domestic cock will beckon young hens with a special cry to a specially prepared nesting place, which he immediately vacates when a hen approaches.

The various sounds described above are only a brief summary of the most important vocal signals and expressions of feeling which have been studied so far. It is interesting to note that the range of sounds of the domestic fowl exceeds that of the fowl in the wild.

Comfort Behaviour

Alongside all these stimulating events in their lives, hens still find time for more contemplative things. After the early-morning peak of activity at sunrise – between 5.00 and 7.00 a.m. – when feeding and egg laying take place, there follows a so-called 'comfort behaviour' period during which hens preen their feathers and, towards midday, doze in a dust-bath or in cool places. A completely undisturbed setting is important for preening, for only then – when they feel secure – will the almost inaccessible parts of the body be properly cleaned using the beak.

Dust-baths in cool dust, earth or sand are very popular. The hens squat down and shake themselves with movements of the body and wings so that their feathers are covered with dust, earth or sand. They then relax with their wings spread open and rest on the cool surface. If domestic fowl take baths in wood ash in a sand box, this can protect them against vermin infestation. Once the dust-bath has been completed, the birds give their powdered feathers a thorough shake and return to the search for food.

In the afternoon, towards 5.00 p.m., a second peak of activity occurs, when the sexual activity of the hen is particularly noticeable. The time just before sunset is taken up with a thorough search for food in order to fill their crops for the night; birds in the wild also use this time to seek out a suitable place to sleep.

Sleeping

Chickens will only sleep in intimate groups, and only when a safe place has been found. It is impossible for wild or domestic fowl to sleep in a strange or insecure situation.

Hens dust bathing – nature's way of controlling parasites

Hens need a perch for roosting at night

When sleeping, chickens sit upright on a perch in their houses, a small distance from the next bird and without regard for the order of precedence – provided that the perches are set at an equal height. If there are perches at different heights, there will be trouble every evening because the lower-ranking birds will enter the house first to sit on the preferred perches at the top, only to be ousted shortly afterwards by the birds that come first in the 'pecking order'. Therefore, perches should all be placed at the same height. With time, many birds will grow accustomed to a particular perch.

Once they have taken up their positions, chickens make a gentle, clucking sound, retract their necks and open and shut their eyes a few times. Then, shutting their eyes, they finally put their heads under a wing and sleep. Any unusual noise will produce considerable panic, but they will quickly settle down again if they are in a very dark environment.

The Pecking Order

The order of precedence in a group of chickens is firmly established by the pecking order. This develops slowly

Above: *White Cochin cockerel*
Left: *Gold Brahma cockerel*
Below: *A pair of Polands*

Blue-grey Old English Game cockerel

Chickens make use of their perching rails in the day-time too – they make useful vantage points

hen, birds fight by pecking their opponents on the neck, head, comb and face; at times, they will flap their wings a little in order to gain better access to the other bird's vulnerable parts.

How fierce the battle will be depends on whether the opponent's appearance is perceived as threatening (an erect, proud posture, a large red comb, arched eyes, folded cheeks); and whether a fight is to continue depends on a hen's confidence. If a bird loses a fight, it will adopt a subservient posture (legs bent, body lowered, movement away from the other bird) to show that it has accepted a lower position in the order of precedence.

The larger a hen's comb is – i.e. the more 'masculine' she is – the more she will be feared by the others. If the comb is changed just a little, the others will regard her as an alien and will attack. Birds with small combs are regarded as harmless by the rest of the group and are forced into lower positions.

The two most pugnacious hens (if there *are* two within the group), will fight the hardest battle for first position in the pecking order, and they will not stop until one bird is beaten. If there is no cockerel in the group, the highest-ranking hen will perform the male role. She will seek out food for the group and even crow; she may even attempt to cover the other hens. (This usually happens with old hens since, over time, they produce fewer female hormones.)

Once the fighting is over and a clear winner has emerged, the pecking order will be firmly established.

but from an early age. At the age of only two to three weeks, chicks will peck at younger ones; later, playful power games will be on the agenda. At puberty – 10 to 12 weeks for hens and 12 to 16 weeks for cockerels – serious, violent battles will start, but the positions of power thus achieved will not develop into a real pecking order until the birds are mature at around 26 weeks.

If a group of chickens includes a cockerel, he is unquestionably at the top of the pecking order. Below him, or if there are no cockerels, hens will fight one another to establish their own order of precedence. Cockerel or

The cockerel normally dominates a group of hens

Young hens which have not previously had any position in the pecking order will require several days to establish one, whereas older birds will achieve this within a few hours of entering a new group.

The highest ranking hen wields power over the others; she possesses all rights, though she does not always exercise them. In general, where there is a clear order of precedence, hints from the highest-ranking hen will suffice to obtain the desired reaction in those of lower status. However, as soon as a bird becomes seriously ill, or when a hen is removed from the group, or when several hens are introduced to it, the whole process will start again.

In this new contest, previously high-ranking birds that have shown signs of weakness will be attacked the most, even by hitherto lower-ranking birds. If the newly introduced birds are of a different colour, it will no longer be the comb size that is important, but the plumage. If one of these birds with a different colouring wins a prominent position in the first fight, this position of power will be imputed to the other birds of that breed, so that one breed will take precedence over another.

The older the hens, the more self-confident their behaviour will be. Thus, if a hen which had previously enjoyed a high rank is introduced, she will bravely expect an even higher position in the new group. Conversely, if low-ranking hens are introduced, they will be very timid and will tend to expect an even lower position, even if their physical characteristics deserve a higher rank in the new group. If disputes arise in connection with low-ranking birds when group changes occur, the highest ranking will take an active part in the fight.

Cockerels and Supremacy

It is a different story when a cockerel is introduced for, by his very presence, he has a conciliatory effect: a cockerel will always assume the highest position. This does not, however, apply to cockerels that grew up in a flock without an adult cockerel. They will have become so intimidated by the aggressive behaviour of the hens that they will be unable to mate. Often a hen will initiate a fight and then succumb so as to allow the cockerel to establish his position.

A similar thing occurs with young cockerels that have grown up in a group led by a cockerel. Here, too, they have become so accustomed to the aggressive behaviour of the highest-ranking bird that they are never able to cover a hen: the higher-ranking cockerel will always intervene Even when the latter has been physically inferior to the younger

Black Rosecomb hen
Brown Leghorn cockerel

White Wyandotte hen
Barnevelder hen

Right: *Cuckoo Maran cockerel*
Below: *Russian Orloff pair*

ones for a long time, their memory of the protracted period when they were the weaker party prevents the younger cockerels from making a bid for supremacy.

If eggs are no longer being fertilized properly due to the size of a group or the age of a cockerel, you should not simply introduce a new cockerel. If the old cockerel loses his position of power, he will become mentally disturbed and waste away in misery.

If, on the other hand, a newcomer is beaten, he will not mate with the hens either; and ensuring that he does not will become the full-time new preoccupation of the older cockerel and he will have no more time to fertilize eggs.

The best approach is either to kill the old cockerel or to introduce two new fully grown cockerels to the group. This will result in three families being produced, for whereas two cockerels will fight one another, three will not.

At moulting time – i.e. when feathers are being replaced in the autumn – the cockerel loses his interest in power and even keeps the hens from food; he will even tolerate another. The highest ranking hens, on the other hand, remain as despotic as ever during the moulting season.

Status of Broody Hens

Battling for order of precedence within a group always upsets egg production. Not until each bird knows its position in the group and thus feels safe within it, can normal egg production begin.

When establishing a group of hens, it should therefore be borne in mind that it should not consist of more than 30 birds. This is the maximum number that will be able to identify one another in accordance with the established order of precedence.

The powers of memory of chickens vary considerably, so any member of the group that tries to segregate itself, such as a broody hen, should always be kept within visual contact. Separate her by all means, but only by a fence.

Broodies do try to secede from the rest of their group for their brooding time, even attempting to frighten the others off by using some rather feeble threatening postures; and these attempts at separation from the group will not be looked on favourably by the other hens.

If a broody hen then gets into a situation where she needs to defend her place in the pecking order, although in her brooding condition she is quite incapable of doing so, her weakness is soon recognized and

Broody hens lose their aggression and so run the risk of falling to the bottom of the pecking order

reduced comb

looser plumage

taken avantage of without mercy. All her fellow hens will peck at her fiercely.

If the broody hen has not been kept within visual contact of the group, there will be problems afterwards with re-integration. Most birds will by then have forgotten what position she occupied in the pecking order, or indeed the pecking order may have altered because of her absence. If, on the other hand, the broody has only been separated from the rest of the group by a wire fence, she will not be forgotten.

Young hens that have grown up together as chicks under a broody hen tend to find it easier than other birds to fit into a group. However, through breeding it has become possible to produce less pugnacious breeds that quickly establish an order of precedence. Among the particularly aggressive breeds are Italian ones (Anconas and/or Leghorns) and New Hampshire, whereas Australorps are far more peaceable.

Mating

Wild chickens live in groups varying between 16 and 40 cocks and hens. Sometimes there is more than one hen to a cock, though often they are paired one to one. Superfluous hens form separate groups in a no-man's-land between neighbouring groups.

In the mating season – April to October – the cockerel approaches a hen and stands very erect in front of her, with his neck feathers ruffled. He then proceeds to dance around her, with the wing nearest her spread

Mating birds need to use their wings to help sustain their balance. The cock bird grips the hen by the nape of the neck

downwards as he struts around.

Alternatively, he may stalk the hen with wing spread downwards and his tail fanned out behind him; the hen, thus intimidated, then ducks down and allows mating to take place. Often the cock will use food to attract the hens for mating – 'wooing at a distance'.

High-ranking hens will often avoid mating by flying off and emitting cries of varying intensity, whereas lower-ranking birds will duck down willingly. With a lower-ranking hen, it is frequently enough for a cock just to rear himself up in front of her with neck feathers ruffled, as a dominant gesture: the hen will at once duck down for mating. The frequency of copulation increases with the size of the open space available and the smallness of the group. With domestic chickens, however, the mating ceremony is not so clearly defined.

In order to mate, the cock (domestic or wild) jumps on to the shoulders of the squatting hen, having first pecked her neck with his beak and got a firm grip. The hen lowers her head and raises her tail feathers and rump

Left: *Speckled Sussex hen*
Above: *Light Sussex hen*

Derbyshire Redcap pair

Rhode Island Red hen

Plymouth Rock pullet

so that the cock can press his cloaca against that of the hen to transfer his sperm. The cloaca serves a dual purpose in both sexes: in the hen, it is responsible for defecation and egg-laying; in the male, as well as dealing with defecation, it acts as a spermatic duct.

With domestic chickens, not every act of copulation is accompanied by the secretion of sperm. In addition, the mating 'homage' ceremony (in which the cock properly mounts the hen for a second time), observed in the wild, occurs in only a perfunctory fashion among domestic fowl.

After the mating season, the wild cock loses his sex drive and goes into a partial moult – that is, he changes his splendid plumage for his 'plain clothes'. His behaviour, too, now becomes less self-confident and more reserved.

Laying

Two or three days after mating, the first fertilized egg may be laid, and fertilization will continue for about four days. Domestic hens now begin to cluck straight after mating; wild hens, on the other hand, will not cluck until shortly before laying.

In response, the wild cock will look for a suitable nest, a protected hollow in the ground in which the hen, by moving her body backwards and forwards, is able to make herself comfortable without needing to bother about additional nest material. Here she lays her six to eight eggs, taking about two hours to lay each one, at intervals of about 30 hours. In between laying, she calmly re-establishes contact with the flock, which will be no more than 30 to 50 m (100-165 ft) away.

In the case of the domestic hen, the cock also looks for a nest for the hen when she is about to lay, and entices her towards it. Laying takes place in just the same way as with the wild hen, except that domestic hens lay between five and seven eggs, depending on the breed, and this can be repeated a number of times throughout the year. Wild hens have a maximum of two small batches containing a total of eight to twelve eggs per year, primarily in May and October.

The wild hen sits on her nest after laying the eggs, whereas this instinct has often been bred out of domestic hens. Many breeders prefer to hatch large quantities of eggs in an incubator instead of having a hen sit on 12 to 15 of them, since she will stop laying while brooding and rearing. Because this is 'unproductive', modern hybrids have now been 'freed' from this activity; however, when kept free range, some of these hybrids can revert to broody behaviour.

The eggs of these birds should not be taken for breeding purposes: because they have been obtained from several crossings in a complex selection process, their high performance is only applicable to the current generation; the next generation is often weak.

Signs of Broodiness

Both wild and domestic hens mate

Broodies leave the nest only once a day, and sometimes have to be persuaded to do so

once or twice a year, and when they begin to incubate their eggs – i.e. become broody – their whole behaviour changes. A few days before they take up their sitting position, they produce rolling clucking sounds, remain for long periods on as full a nest as possible, and peck if an attempt is made to lift them. At the same time, they ruffle their neck feathers and threaten with a rapid warbling sound.

When they are sitting on the nest, the metabolism of both wild and domestic fowl changes considerably, while their body temperature remains the same. They will only leave the nest once a day, mostly at midday. At this time, their predators in the wild are resting, whereas in the chicken yard there tends to be a quieter atmosphere. They can therefore eat, drink and defecate unmolested for the most part.

At this noontime meal, a hen will consume around 40 g (1½ oz) of grain, an amount that, normally, would not be sufficient for her requirements. She will also perform her one defecation of the day, as opposed to her usual more frequent ones. She

also takes a dust-bath and then, in the case of the wild hen, makes her way by a circuitous route back to the nest. Nevertheless, she is now leading a dangerous existence, for predators are constantly on the look-out. Older hens are better able to protect themselves than younger, inexperienced ones.

Hatching and Early Life

The embryo begins to grow in the fertilized egg while it is still in the hen's oviduct, and this continues after the egg has been laid, but only in response to the warmth produced in brooding. Oxygen is carried through the shell into the membranes where it is distributed by means of the blood circulation.

From Day 12 of brooding, the embryo is sensitive to noise. On Day 17, the embryo breaks through the egg's membrane so that its head and beak are outside the inner body of the egg, in the air pocket. The chicks are now breathing with their lungs, are aware of their mother's clucking and imprint it in their memories. Shortly before hatching, they answer with a loud cheeping sound.

The chicks also have contact with one another, being sensitive to each other's calls. All the chicks in a clutch develop similarly, and they will usually, as a result of these calls, hatch simultaneously. The ones that are ready to hatch will wait for up to two hours for stragglers to prepare themselves for hatching. The hen offers no assistance at all in the hatch-

Left: *Silver Laced Poland hen*
Below left: *Gold Pencilled Hamburgh hen*
Below right: *Silver Spangled Hamburgh hen*
Bottom left: *Ancona hen*
Bottom right: *Welsummer cockerel*
Right: *Silver Laced Wyandotte hen*

ing process but waits quietly sitting on the eggs.

Using the egg-tooth on their beaks, the chicks saw through the shells, and by the end of Day 21, almost all of the chicks have hatched. Only if eggs have been laid over a relatively long period of time will further chicks hatch later than this.

Feeding off the yolk sac in their stomachs, chicks will need no other nourishment for at least 24 hours. This is useful because wild and domestic chicks alike first need to get to know their environment and peck at whatever is of interest around them.

Imprinting

At this point, the chicks go through a very short 'imprinting' period, which lasts for about 36 hours and is at its height between the 13th and 16th hour. This explains why chicks should *not* be removed from the mother hen until all of them have hatched: what they miss now cannot be made up at a later stage.

During imprinting, the chicks are at a very sensitive stage characterized mainly by a freedom from fear. The following is a typical behavioural pattern. To begin with, chicks react equally to substitute broody hens – e.g. a cardboard box which is made to emit a call signal – but during these first hours, the signals from their own kind have such a strong effect that, in a very short time, they will show a preference for their own kind rather than the artificial hen, and will follow the real one. The closer the imprinting period comes to its conclusion, the more anxious the chicks will be to

act in accordance with the characteristic behavioural pattern.

After three days or so, they are familiar with their companions and already able to assess what is good to eat, while at the same time the broody hen is still devotedly caring for them. She looks for food for her young, calling them with her typical clucking sound; she then pecks at the food, lets it drop, and repeats this process until the chicks themselves start to peck at it. They will also eat soft food from the side of her beak.

It is now that they eagerly learn from the broody hen how to scratch with their beaks and feet in order to find food in the ground, how to cut up food with their beaks, how to sharpen their beaks by scraping them on the ground, and how to shake their heads to remove the sticky remains of food. (Unfortunately, it sometimes happens that, as a result of the lively, pronounced shaking movements of the hen, a chick is knocked sideways and killed.)

Wild hens put a great deal more effort into nurturing the chicks and offer food at the mere sight of them. For the domestic hen, it is their cheeping sound and not the sight of them that triggers this response.

Recognition

Chicks and broody hens recognize one another, though the chicks are better able to recognize their mother than the other way round. (I have, however, observed cases in which the opposite has occurred.) Due to the vocal recognition factor, there are rarely cases of mistaken identity, but if they do occur, they are quickly sorted out.

Strange chicks will be fought off by the broody hen at once; indeed, the wild hen has no hesitation in killing them. Consideration might be given to a domestic broody hen hatching her own eggs; however, the establishing of contact in the egg and the first hours after hatching are decisive.

Independence and Maturity

In the first days, the hen and her chicks keep to a small area of no more than 2 sq m (6½ sq ft). After 10 to 12 days, the chicks start to roam wider, but immediately return to the hen when they perceive danger. Their sense of direction improves and they begin to remember the layout of their living quarters. By Day 14, the chicks seem to lead the hen around, and it is no longer the hen that takes the initiative.

After five weeks they have sufficient feather covering not to need to sleep close to the hen any longer. Shortly after the 8th week, the broody hen begins to peck at the young male chicks and severs the last maternal bonds. Her hormones are now geared for egg-laying, and her maternal instinct disappears.

The chicks must now be introduced to the community of fully grown birds, which can only take place with the battles for precedence described above. It is worth noting that chicks brought up by a broody hen have fewer problems with the pecking order because they have already got used to authority. Chicks that have not been trained by a broody hen react far more aggressively.

Chicks born in the wild have a poor survival rate. Out of 100 chicks hatched, around 25 per cent reach the age of 8 to 10 weeks, and of these only about a quarter (i.e. six) survive the first year.

The natural lifespan of the domestic hen is about 20 years. Although, in exceptional cases, a few eggs may still be laid in their 12th year, in general egg-laying activity decreases significantly after the 3rd year. As they age, the health of the birds is not particularly good, moulting becomes burdensome and they become increasingly cantankerous. If a hen is destined for the cooking pot, this should take place by the time it is three years old; any later, and the meat will be less edible.

In conclusion, I would say that the domestication of chickens has reduced their fear. Better feeding conditions, less stress (if they are kept properly!) and selective breeding have resulted in a series of striking changes: more fleshy birds (i.e. the heavy breeds); an enormous egg-laying capacity; a reduction in their instinctive and ritualistic behaviour in favour of a slower but enhanced learning capacity; and a more highly developed social behaviour, making greater use of communication through vocal signals.

This increased learning capacity and ability to adapt well to different lifestyles and climates – quite apart from the financial benefits – are responsible for the popularity of domestic chickens today.

Breeds of Chickens

There is a bewilderingly large number of breeds, and to begin with, choosing which one to keep can be difficult. First, you need to clarify in your own mind why the hens are going to be kept. What do you want?

- A large quantity of eggs
- A large quantity of meat
- Brooding or non-brooding hens
- Lively birds that are able to fly
- Quiet birds with no interest in flying
- Ornamental fowl

Also an important factor to consider is the size of the available run.

There are five main groups of domestic breeds:

- The Mediterranean type
- The North-west European type
- The Asiatic type
- Dwarf breeds/bantams
- Hybrids

Among the Mediterranean group are the **Minorca**, the **Leghorn**, and the **Ancona**. Typical representatives of the North-west European type are the **Hamburgh**, the **Barnevelder** and the **North Holland Blue**. Among the Asiatic types are the **Brahma**, the **Silkie** and the **Cochin**. As regards the dwarf breeds, a distinction is made between those produced by selective breeding (e.g. the **Bantam Ancona**) and bantams proper (e.g. **Sebright**).

The following table is only a selection of the breeds which are now available. For a complete listing, refer to published works on national poultry standards.

TABLE OF CHICKEN BREEDS

Breed	Origin
Large fowl:	
Barnevelder	Netherlands
Cochin	Asia
Hamburgh	North Europe
Indian Game	Britain
Leghorn	Mediterranean
Maran	France
New Hampshire Red	USA
Orpington	Britain
Plymouth Rock	USA
Rhode Island Red	USA
Silkie	Asia
Sussex	Britain

Classification	Plumage	Weight
Heavy	Two main varieties: Double Laced and Partridge. Also Black, Silver	Cock 3.2-3.6 kg (7-8 lb) Hen 2.7-3.2 kg (6-7 lb)
Heavy	Black, Blue, Buff, Cuckoo, Partridge, Grouse and White varieties. Full leg feathering	Cock 4.5-5.9 kg (10-13 lb) Hen 4-5 kg (9-11 lb)
Light	Black and Gold varieties; and pencilled and spangled varieties of each	Cock 2.3 kg (5 lb) Hen 1.8 kg (4 lb)
Heavy	Predominantly black and green plumage with brown ground colour	Cock 3.6 kg (8 lb) minimum Hen 2.7 kg (6 lb) minimum
Light	12 varieties	Cock 3.4 kg (7½ lb) Hen 2.5 kg (5½ lb)
Heavy	Black, Dark Cuckoo, Golden Cuckoo, Silver Cuckoo varieties	Cock 3.6 kg (8 lb) Hen 3.2 kg (7 lb)
Heavy	Reddish bay and chestnut brown plumage	Cock 3.9 kg (8½ lb) Hen 2.9 kg (6½ lb)
Heavy	Black, Blue, Buff and White varieties	Cock 4.5-6.4 kg (10-14 lb) Hen 3.4-4.8 kg (7½-10½ lb)
Heavy	Barred, Black, Buff, Columbian and White varieties	Cock 3.9-4.8 kg (8½-10½ lb) Hen 2.7-3.6 kg (6-8 lb)
Heavy	Rich brilliant red plumage, with black	Cock 3.9 kg (8½ lb) Hen 2.9 kg (6½ lb)
Light	Black, Blue, Gold and White varieties; full feathering on legs	Cock 1.4 kg (3 lb) Hen 0.9 kg (2 lb)
Heavy	Brown, Buff, Red, Speckled, Silver and White varieties	Cock 4 kg (9 lb) minimum Hen 3.2 kg (7 lb) minimum

Pure breeds should only be obtained from specialist breeders. If you buy birds from a market, from travelling poultry sellers or from mixed poultry suppliers, you will almost always end up with hybrids. These will be breeds which, as a result of extensive crossing, can give a good yield for a single generation, whereas any offspring will usually be unproductive. High-performance hybrids are therefore always selected for one generation, not for breeding, and sold to poultry farms; after two years of high output, these birds will need to be replaced. In addition to this, for the production of chickens destined for the table – broilers – the chicks are fattened up to be ready for the table within seven or eight weeks, long before they are ready to breed.

The table summarizes the characteristics of different breeds. However, you should always remember that, even within a breed, no one hen will be the same as another (here too, fortunately, you will find individuals!), and that the way in which the birds are kept will significantly affect their development.

There are special egg-layers with very little meat on them, all-rounders with good egg and meat production, and typically meat-producing birds.

One interesting, economical meat producer is the **Bantam Welsummer**, which obtains the bulk of its comparatively small diet naturally in the run, even catching insects in flight! Heavy breeds are disinclined to do this, being somewhat slower birds, and are quite happy to have their food placed in front of their beaks.

TABLE OF CHICKEN BREEDS

Breed	Origin
Welsummer	Netherlands
Wyandotte	USA
Bantams:	
Ancona	Mediterranean
Frizzle	Many countries
Old English Game	Britain
Sebright	Britain

Buying Chickens

What should you buy – chicks, pullets, broody hens with eggs, or broody hens with chicks?

Broiler chicks – that is, chicks of both sexes – of a meat-type breed, need to be kept in appropriate conditions for 10 to 12 weeks before they are ready for slaughter. They are relatively cheap to buy.

If, on the other hand, you want to produce your own eggs as quickly as possible, it is a lot easier to buy 10 'point of lay' (POL) pullets, perhaps with a cockerel.

Classification	Plumage	Weight
Light	Rich golden brown, plus black with green sheen; also Silver Duckwing variety (black-and-white)	Cock 3.2 kg (7 lb) Hen 2.7 kg (6 lb)
Heavy	13 varieties	Cock 3.6-4 kg (8-9 lb) Hen 3.2 kg (7 lb)
Miniature of Ancona breed	Beetle-green with v-shaped white feather tips	Cock 560-620 g (20-22 oz) Hen 510-620 g (18-22 oz)
Miniature of many breeds	Frizzled feathers in the colours of the original breed	Cock 680-780 g (24-28 oz) Hen 560-680 g (20-24 oz)
Developed from common bantam fowl	Very numerous colours	Cock 620-730 g (22-26 oz) Hen 510-620 g (18-22 oz)
Genuine bantam	Gold and Silver varieties	Cock 620 g (22 oz) Hen 510 g (18 oz)

Hybrids

If you have no intention of breeding, or intend to buy hatching eggs for a broody hen from a breeder at a later date, you can go for hybrids. Generally speaking, one in ten of these hens, if kept properly, will turn out to be a broody hen.

Make sure that the birds have not been de-beaked. Beaks should be smooth at the front, and rounded towards the end with a slight tip. When hybrid hens are kept in cages, the beak is often shortened to prevent them from pecking one another, but this also has a considerable effect on their food and water consumption!

Normal hen (left) and debeaked hen (right)

shining comb

bright eyes

clean beak

wings held high
and close to body

shiny wattle

unsoiled rear

good feather cover

smooth-skinned legs

undeformed feet

Points of a healthy hen

Where to Buy

You will find the names of breeders of different types of chickens in magazines dealing with poultry, farming and small-holding – whatever titles are available in your area. You will find the widest choice in spring.

The prices of pure-bred birds are much higher than those of hybrids. Day-old chicks of both sexes cost around the price of a dozen eggs (as a rough guide) but the prices vary greatly. Young birds cost anything from five to 20 times this amount, depending on rarity of the breed.

If you want a few broilers or pullets, it is a good idea to buy them as day-old chicks either from a market or from a poultry-breeding farm.

If you want to buy broody hens with hatching eggs or already hatched chicks, please remember that being transported by rail is not something that hens enjoy: they need to be left in peace, as undisturbed as possible, if they are to perform well. You should instead try to obtain the hen and her offspring from a nearby source. Find out from your local poultry club whether the breed you are interested in can be found locally. If not, buy a broody hen of a different breed and have the eggs of your chosen breed sent to you.

In all cases, all newly acquired livestock should be kept in quarantine – i.e. separate from other poultry – for the first 14 days so that any diseases which may have been imported will not be passed on to the other birds.

When to Buy

Day-old chicks for use as broilers or pullets should be bought in the spring (April/May in the northern hemisphere). Broody hens with hatching eggs should not be bought before the middle of April, and broody hens with chicks not before the beginning of May. If the weather in May is bad, you will have to ensure that there is dry space for them.

Judging a Hen

It is not at all easy for the beginner to judge a hen; it takes time to acquire an eye for what characterizes a healthy bird, its age and its laying ability. Basically, the feathers should lie flat (except in the moulting season); they should be glossy, clean and tufted, especially in the cloaca region. The bird should move normally, considering its surroundings, and its eyes should protrude slightly and glisten, and react inquisitively to everything around it.

A fully grown laying hen has a space between the legs into which it should be possible to place three fingers. A narrower distance than this indicates that the hen no longer lays or, in the case of a young hen, that she is not yet laying.

The breast should never feel hard. However, the colour and shape of the comb and wattles, the leg colour, the face and the beak differ considerably depending on the breed and can only provide useful information to the experienced breeder.

Light breeds betray their age by the length of the spur (the rear toe of the foot). Young hens up to the age of six months have a small finger-nail-shaped point which soon grows bigger and, by two years, exceeds 2 cm (¾ in) in length. A hen breeder once showed me how to determine a bird's age in months by counting the rings on its leg. However, I cannot be certain whether this applies to all breeds.

Brooding

If you are interested in keeping hens that will brood – that is, hens that will sit on a nest to incubate eggs until they hatch – it is essential to choose the right eggs. Since no two hens are the same (and so will not begin brooding at the same time), and only eggs from the best birds should be used, it is advisable to begin a few weeks before the hoped-for brooding by collecting the eggs from good laying hens.

Choosing Eggs

Young hens will start to lay in the autumn even though they will not be fully grown until the spring. However, the best eggs for hatching are those from fully grown (i.e. two-year-old) birds. Then, after two years, the quality of eggs for hatching purposes begins to fall. If only young hens are available, use the eggs from the first batch laid.

Eggs suitable for hatching should be of average size, neither undersized nor oversized – the so-called 'double-yolked' eggs. Anyone who thinks that a double yolk will give a better chance of success will be disappointed: no chick development takes place in these.

The surface of every egg is covered by a protective layer of wax. This is not even removed when eggs that are going to be eaten are washed (otherwise they would go off too quickly). Despite this protection, only clean eggs should be considered for brooding. Apart from anything else, soiled eggs are not a good indication of correct keeping; rather, they tend to signal dirty, uncared-for nest boxes or some form of diarrhoea in the hens.

Eggs should be neither cracked nor strongly pigmented – i.e. one end must not be darker than the other. However, a shell that is uniformly dark in colour means that it is the first particularly rich egg in the laying series. Calcium deposits in the form of ridges or spots are also undesirable; they prevent the even flow of air, moisture and warmth, and also make hatching more difficult. Eggs with large pores are unsuitable, too. Therefore, only eggs with quite smooth surfaces should be used. Eggs for hatching should not be more than 10 to 14 days old at the start of brooding if the vitality of the embryo and the quality of the nutrients are to be at their best.

'Candling' Eggs

It is also necessary to check the inside of the egg. For this, you should use what is known as a 'candling' box, and this can be easily made at home. Use the box in as dark a room as possible. When the eggs are placed over the opening, above the lamp, any

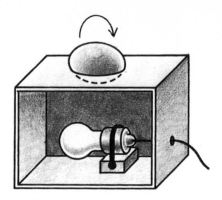

Candling hatching eggs over a bright light in a home-made candling box

dark spots that show through the shells will be blood spots. Eggs containing blood spots can certainly be eaten, but they will be unsuitable for hatching.

Blood spots occur most frequently in young laying hens, in medium-sized breeds and in very productive laying hens. They may also occur in birds when nest boxes and perches are positioned too high. When the yolk is discharged from the egg store, a blood vessel is sometimes detached with it; this blood spot remains on the yolk.

It is also quite easy to identify shells of uneven thickness and with hairline cracks by using a 'candling' box. Eggs with such characteristics should be rejected. You should also make sure that the air space is at the larger end of the egg.

Caring for your Chosen Eggs

The date of laying and possibly the name or foot-ring number of the hen should be marked on the egg with a pencil. The eggs should be stored in a cool place (at around 10-14°C [50-57°F]) where it is not too dry (around 75 per cent air humidity). Every day they should be turned halfway round on their longitudinal axis; the details pencilled on to the egg can be used as indicators for this. A broody hen will turn the eggs she is looking after some eight times a day using her beak; this is to prevent the egg membranes from adhering to the shell.

Up to 5 eggs are collected per hen each week. However, you should always keep only the eggs from the most recent week; the older eggs can be used for immediate consumption. This process is continued until one or more of the hens become broody.

Preparing the Hen

The broody hen should be free of any parasites at this time. If her housing is cleaned out regularly, the only preventive measure required will be a dust-bath. Birds that carry parasites despite this will need to be treated

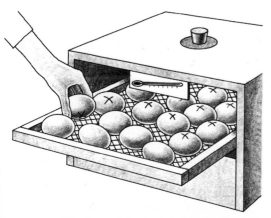

Eggs that are being incubated artificially should be turned once every day

with an insect powder which can be obtained from the vet. However, due to the humid warmth produced by the hen when brooding, a certain amount of the powder's ingredients can find their way through the porous shells of the eggs she is hatching. Hens should, therefore, be examined and, if necessary, treated some time in advance of the expected brooding period.

If several hens become broody at the same time or in quick succession, they can be kept in the same housing. However, under no circumstances should broodies be kept with hens that are not brooding because the former need to be left undisturbed to do their job. If they are kept together in the hen-house, the broodies will either be disturbed by the others and be obstructed in the run, or they will begin to sit on each other's nests at random because their places have been taken by other hens while they were out for food.

The best set-up is for each broody to have her own small run, but still within sight of the other hens. At some distance from the nest should be the box for use as a dust-bath, a container of grain, a drinker and a bowl of sand and small stones. Vegetable leftovers may also be given, but no soft food. The ground in the housing should be covered with untreated sawdust or sand.

When Brooding Begins

Hopefully by now, you have a sufficient quantity of usable eggs, and your broody hen has been clucking for two or three days, and wandering

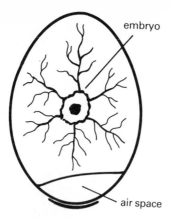

embryo

air space

Fertile egg on the sixth day of incubation

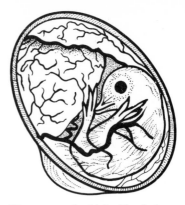

The same egg after 14 days' incubation

around looking for a suitable place to sit. You now need to take the hen into her hen-house in the evening; she may try to defend herself with fierce pecking, so it is best to wear a pair of heavy-duty gloves when moving her.

The eggs (10 to 15 in number), which you will already have placed in the nest, have been lying all day in semi-darkness. If you have had the eggs sent to you, they should not be moved unduly for two days before brooding starts. However, do not forget the daily turning of the eggs along their longitudinal axis!

Finally, your broody hen gets down to the serious business of incubating her eggs. Once a day, she will leave the nest to eat, drink, defecate and take a dust-bath. At these times, the eggs cool off, but this is important for their development.

The broody hen will turn the eggs several times a day with her beak. The moist warmth from her body is sufficient to moisten the surface of the eggs. However, eggs from New Hampshire hens are sometimes quite thick-walled and the membranes so

tough that supplementary sprinkling with tepid water can help the hatching process. If duck or goose eggs are being hatched, these must be given additional moisture daily (*see* Ducks and Geese).

On the 6th day, the eggs must be candled again. (Eggs of a very dark colour are best candled a second time a day or two later.) While this is being done, warm up some plaster eggs and place them under the broody. The candling box should show what looks like a spider's web, in the middle of which can be found a slightly moving circle – the embryo. If the embryo has stopped growing, this web will not be seen, and the egg should be rejected.

Eggs that have not developed properly should be boiled for half an hour, shelled, chopped up and put in an appropriate container for freezing. Later, this can be mixed with greens and used as chick food two days after the rest of the chicks have hatched.

If unfertilized eggs or eggs in which the embryos have died remain in the nest, they will very quickly go off, ferment, crack open and soil both the other eggs and the hen, thus endangering the whole brood. If this unfortunate situation should arise, all the remaining eggs must be given a quick hosing down with tepid water and laid in clean straw to dry; the hen, too, must be cleaned around the abdomen if her feathers have been soiled.

The same applies if the hen should accidentally break an egg. This is particularly common with heavy breeds; however, because of their body size, they are able to cover a large number of eggs, and they often make particularly good broodies. Or it may be that the eggs are thin-shelled; this may be a characteristic of the breed in question (for example, Leghorns tend to have quite thin shells) or it may be due to calcium deficiency.

For safety's sake, the eggs are again candled on the 14th day. By now, the embryo almost fills the egg, thus blocking out most of the light; light should only be seen coming through the large end, where the air space is located. Any eggs not fitting this pattern should be removed and thrown on to the compost heap, after you have first cracked the shells. It is important to crack them, otherwise they might rot inside and then burst open, producing an obnoxious smell. In general, however, all the eggs should have developed well if they were properly candled on the 6th day.

Hatching

Shortly before hatching, the chicks take in the yolk sac via the umbilical cord, which then closes up behind it.

Chicks do not 'peck' the shell open when they hatch – they push against it with the special 'egg tooth' on the top of their beaks

By Day 20, the first eggs are chipped, though the chicks do not actually peck through the shell – there is too little space for that. Until just before hatching, the chick's head is pushed forward over the chest and tucked under one of the wings. Then the chick raises its head, and the egg-tooth on top of the beak presses a hole in the shell.

By slowly rotating on its own axis, using the inside wall of the egg to push against, the chick eventually makes a circular hole in the shell near its head, until, by extending its neck, it is able to lift the 'cap' it has formed. Throughout hatching, the broody hen plays no part, except to keep calm!

During the course of Day 21, most of the chicks will have hatched. On rare occasions, a chick may hatch with the 'cap' of shell placed so awkwardly over its head that it is unable to free itself. In such cases, you can assist it by carefully lifting off the shell and, if necessary, removing any bits of shell from the nest. If bits of shell get stuck to the chicks, you can free them by carefully wetting the pieces of shell with a small sponge and removing them.

However, in general, it is wrong to help chicks hatch. You could cause injury, and in any case, chicks, if they are viable, should be able to hatch by themselves. Chicks that are too weak to do so are not likely to survive the first few hours, of if they do, they will soon fall ill and possibly infect the healthy chicks. So the rule should be: interfere as little as possible; if you do, you may only cause harm, and the hen will become nervous.

After Hatching

Chicks that have just hatched look rather wet. However, this is not due to any moisture: because of the cramped quarters inside the egg, their downy feathers are enclosed in horny sheaths. These break open once the chick has hatched, turning into a powder which soon falls off, and the feathers are free to unfold.

Chicks do not need anything to eat for the first 24 hours; the yolk sac in their stomachs is a rich source of nourishment. However, they should have access to water from a chick drinker.

A broody hen should be able to cope easily with up to 20 chicks. If she is left with fewer than 15, you can place some additional day-old chicks that you have bought under her on the first night; it is important that these new chicks still have the egg-tooth on their beaks.

If some latecomers are yet to hatch, because the eggs used were of widely differing laying dates, the hen is less likely to leave the nest for very long, even with most chicks hatched.

Should she remain off the nest for very long, however, you can bring in an infra-red lamp as a safety precaution, though this should not be placed too close to the nest. It must still be comfortable for the hen to sit on the nest, without being bothered by the heat from the lamp. In most cases, however, she will go straight back to the nest since the chicks will not yet be making excursions beyond the immediate environs of the nest. On no account should the chicks stray far from the hen until the remaining

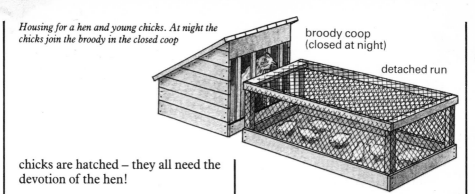

Housing for a hen and young chicks. At night the chicks join the broody in the closed coop

broody coop
(closed at night)

detached run

chicks are hatched – they all need the devotion of the hen!

Incubators

There is little to say in a book of this kind about rearing chicks in an incubator, since the instructions supplied with such equipment may differ somewhat from one model to another. For the beginner, it makes more sense to rear chicks with a broody hen because incubation equipment only earns its keep if it is used continuously.

An alternative is for the beginner to hire an incubator: addresses can be obtained from poultry and farm magazines. However, it is important to ask yourself whether your hobby or a small business could get along just as well without such expenditure.

When a Broody should not Brood

What should you do when a hen becomes broody and this does not fit in with your plans – e.g. the time of year is not right? There have been some quite incredible suggestions of ways to make a broody change back into an ordinary hen, but, in the first place, 99 per cent of these methods are extremely hard on the bird, and in

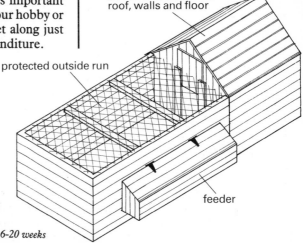

house with insulated roof, walls and floor

protected outside run

feeder

Follow-on housing for pullets of 16-20 weeks

the second place, they do not have much effect.

The most sensible idea I have heard in this connection is to place an inappropriately broody hen with a neighbour's flock; after a week, the hen will have forgotten about brooding and can be returned. Another possibility, and one that will entail rather less stress for the bird, is to let her sit on artificial eggs made of plaster. After 21 days of this, you can try, in the evening, to place two or three male or female chicks beneath her; if the broody takes to these 'step-children', they can easily be brought up with the rest of the stock.

Rearing Chicks

During the weeks following hatching, the broody hen will be preoccupied with caring for her chicks. A good run with bushes for shelter is important now, as is a well-lit, dry hen-house, separated from the older birds, with clean straw on the ground. The latter must be accessible from the run at all times, so that the hen and the chicks can take refuge there in case of danger or bad weather.

When there are a number of broodies with chicks – that is, a 'brood' – a teamwork system often comes about after a few days. In this, one hen goes with the chicks while the others rest, or the hens go on combined excursions with the chicks.

However, sometimes hens do not get on with one another. If a certain broody has had a run to herself and her chicks for a few days, she may resist the introduction of another

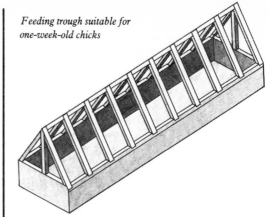

Feeding trough suitable for one-week-old chicks

broody and her chicks. If the resulting quarrels do not stop within a couple of days, the hens will need to be housed separately. On the other hand, a much larger run can make segregation unnecessary, even from the rest of your stock. Nevertheless, a separate hen-house for each broody and her chicks is essential at night.

Early Feeding

You should let the birds out of the hen-house shortly before sunrise. This is when insects and other protein-rich earth life can be readily pecked up from the ground, whereas a couple of hours later, they are hard to find.

In addition to a continuous supply of fresh water from the chick drinker (which should be cleaned daily), food should be placed in shallow plastic feeding bowls, and these should be cleaned thoroughly each time the birds are fed. After the first week, small feeding troughs with grilles are recommended so it is not so easy for the food to become soiled. If the hen seems to be developing too much of a taste for the chicks' food, it will need to be kept from her.

In the first week, chicks will need to be fed six times a day; in the second week, five times a day; and during Weeks 3 and 4, four times a day. Between Weeks 5 and 8, it will be enough to feed them three times a day. Thereafter they can be fed twice a day, as for fully grown birds. The feed troughs should allow 3 cm (1¼ in) of trough space per chick up to three weeks old, and 6 cm (2¼ in) for chicks up to eight weeks old. The more space, the better!

Once the chicks reach eight weeks old, the broody will slowly lose her attachment to her offspring. They can now be kept separately, and the broody will return to her flock.

The Young Cockerels

The cockerels, which are easily recognizable in the light breeds by their larger combs, may now become a great nuisance to the female birds. If there is sufficient space, the best idea is to separate them with a fence, so that the young hens and cockerels are kept apart. Bushes and similar visual protection in the cockerels' run is usually sufficient because then they are not always in the field of vision

A tray of day-old chicks that have been incubated artificially

and confrontations can be more easily avoided.

If the run is very large, and there are frequent scuffles between the hens and cockerels, the latter can be put with the adult birds. It is best to introduce them in the evening, placing them beneath the perches and underneath the manure board, and protecting them with a wire fence from attack by adult birds. During the day, they will be able to see enough to avoid attack in the run, and gradually they will become integrated into the flock.

The young hens should be treated in the same way when they reach the age of about 16 weeks. They will be mature enough to begin laying some time between Weeks 24 and 28.

Ringing

When hens are between 8 and 12 weeks old, they will have to be ringed. This is a particularly important time in the case of special breeds because the closed rings on which the year of hatching is engraved will not fit over the foot any later than this.

It is also important to mark hybrid breeds with rings, so that the age of the birds can be readily established. These plastic or metal rings can be bought from farm suppliers. Plastic rings are more comfortable at extreme temperatures and cause fewer injuries.

Incubated Chicks

Chicks hatched in incubators can be reared in the same way as chicks from broodies, but in this case, it is essen-

Chicks reared artificially will need supplementary heating for the first three weeks .

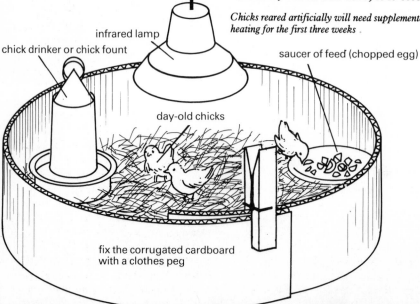

infrared lamp

chick drinker or chick fount

saucer of feed (chopped egg)

day-old chicks

fix the corrugated cardboard with a clothes peg

tial that these unprotected birds be put in a cage-like run. Each day the cage should be moved to a different area of pasture so that the young birds have constant access to fresh greens and do not come into too much contact with their own droppings. Feeding will be the same as for other young chickens.

A wooden box with an infra-red lamp can be useful as housing for the birds in bad weather and at night, and this can communicate with the caged run. The corners of the chicks' new housing should be lined with cardboard or straw; otherwise, the birds may be crushed there, especially in the first week.

It is important that boxes and cages are not too small; there should still be space for the chicks to move freely when they are five to six weeks old. If this is not the case, the run will have to be extended.

After five to six weeks, you should transfer the young birds to a large run that offers protection from predators. Housing that will protect the young birds from bad weather and for use at nights is also still a necessity. However, the best-quality chicken wire will be of no use if the pop-hole (door) to the hen-house is not locked at night.

Foxes, cats and other predators are very clever and will find ways of getting past the fencing. Due to their comparatively poor night vision, hens will be at their mercy, and once the intruders have got a taste for killing, they will continue until not one bird is left alive. So it is imperative, even in summer when a protected run is in use, to close the pop-hole at night.

A Beginner's Introduction to Heredity and Selective Breeding

How do we come by breeds that will always produce the same characteristics, and in what way can changes be produced through breeding? Gregor Mendel (1822-84) studied the problem of heredity and discovered the 'laws' named after him, which are still valid today.

In the nuclei of the cells of all living organisms, there is a given number of *chromosomes*, which is fixed for each species. These are very complex chemical structures, and when viewed through an electron microscope, they look like rope-ladders twisted around their own axes. At specific points along these chromosome rope-ladders are the genes. A gene is basically the trigger for the development of a particular characteristic – e.g. the feather colouring of a hen.

Almost all chromosomes are present in the cells as pairs (i.e. double or diploid chromosome sets). However, in the sex, or germ, cells (known as *gametes*) one half of the chromosomes are missing, so that, at fertilization, pairs are formed with one half of the chromosomes coming from the father and the other half coming from the mother.

For example when fertilization takes place – that is, when the male gamete A combines with the female gamete B – a new cell (AB) is formed,

49

Two pathways of inheritance: (left) intermediate inheritance; (right) dominant-recessive inheritance

and this has a double chromosome set (A + B). This new AB cell is the starting point for the new organism.

'Pure-bred' Animals

If animal A is 'pure-bred', both chromosomes of the chromosome pair will have the same genes for a given characteristic (e.g. black feathers). If animal B is not pure-bred, this means that, on one chromosome, there is a gene for black feathers, for instance, and on the other, a gene for white feathers.

Despite this, both birds may actually have black feathers. In the first case (A), the so-called *phenotype* (external characteristics) and the *genotype* (gene pattern) are uniform. In case B, on the other hand, the genotype does not correspond to the phenotype; however, the genetic blueprint for black feathers has asserted itself because it is strong, or *dominant*, whereas the genetic blueprint for white feathers is weaker, or *recessive*.

Things are often more complicated than this example would indicate because, in some cases, several genes are involved in the determination of a given characteristic, or because of the occurrence of mutations (unexpected changes in the blueprints). In addition, there are a whole host of other special factors that are too complicated to deal with here.

Mendel's Laws

It will be enough for beginners to

familiarize themselves with the two laws of inheritance known as 'Mendel's Laws'. These explain how genetic blueprints are transmitted in different ways over several generations.

1 The Law of Recombination

If the two parents are both pure-bred – e.g. they each have two identical genes in their chromosomes for feather colour – but bird A is pure-bred black while bird B is pure-bred white, the chicks will be mixtures of the parent birds. If two of these chicks are then mated, the second law comes into effect.

2 The Law of Segregation

A separation of the genetic blueprints can now be observed. Supposing that four chicks are hatched. On average, one chick will be black with two identical genes for black (that is, its phenotype (external characteristics) and its genotype are uniform); one of the chicks will be white, in this case with two identical genes for white feathers; and the two remaining chicks will, like their parents, be mixtures, with mixed colouring and two different genes for feather colouring. We thus see a division of the blueprints in the following ratio: 25% pure-bred white, 25% pure-bred black, and 50% intermediate (a mixture of the two). This whole process is known as the *intermediate heredity process*. But there is also another – the *dominant-recessive heredity process*.

Assume that the colour black is dominant and prevails over white (or any other colour). The following will then be observed:

If a pure-bred black hen and a pure-bred white cock are mated, all their chicks will have black feathers (black being the dominant characteristic in this case). All will have the same phenotype, but their genotype will be different – that is, each chick will have two different genes governing feather colouring. Thus, as far as their genotype is concerned, they are first-generation hybrids.

If two of these hybrids are then mated, the 'law of segregation' will again come into effect, and we will once more have the ratio of 1:2:1. But this will only be from the point of view of the genotype, since the colour black is dominant and the birds with two different genes will nevertheless be that colour. The chick with two identical genes for black (pure-bred) is thus black, the two hybrids are black and the fourth chick, with two identical genes for white (pure-bred) is, of course, white. This process can be seen clearly in the diagram.

Inbreeding and Cross-breeding

Inbreeding means the mating of parent birds with their offspring and the mating of the offspring with one another. For the production of special breeds, this form of breeding is very important, though if it is carried out too extensively, it can lead to problems.

So it is necessary from time to time to introduce birds from another 'line' (e.g. other adult birds, but of the same breed) and, occasionally, birds of another breed, although in this case, the newly introduced bird must likely to be pure-bred. These lines are then merged in order to combine additional positive characteristics. But here too it is necessary once in a while, to 'cross-breed' with a hen from outside the normal stock.

Breeding

It is a good idea to keep the breeding stock as small as possible, perhaps one cock and five hens. This will mean that only high-ranking hens, the most vigorous ones, will be mated with the cock. Although, as mentioned earlier, higher-ranking hens are less willing to mate, they are nevertheless important if good stock is to be produced.

If a hen continually lays unfertilized eggs, it may only be necessary to move her to another breeding pen and mate her with a different cock.

In order to be able to breed properly, it is, of course, essential to know which egg comes from which hen. However, after a certain amount of observation, it is fairly easy with a small breeding flock to be able to tell (by their shape and colour) which eggs were laid by which hen. Then you will not have to resort to the use of 'trap nests', which are unpleasant for the birds because they have to wait to be removed after laying their eggs instead of being able to move off the nest at will.

The eggs of a given hen must be placed together with just one broody, without the addition of any other eggs for hatching. Otherwise, it will again not be possible after hatching to tell which chicks are the offspring of which parents.

Hybrid hen – the result of selective breeding

be a female to prevent breeding getting out of control.

If a cock of a different breed were introduced, this could lead to the occurrence of undesirable characteristics which would affect all future stock; whereas in the case of a newly introduced hen of a different breed, only her chicks would be affected. Every so often, of course, it will become necessary to replace the cock, but for this, you can select a new one from the same line.

Many breeders keep a number of lines going – that is, more than one inbreeding process in which the characteristics produced are very

Fertilization and Egg Development

As in all other bird species, the hen has a single ovary, while the male has two testes positioned well inside the abdominal cavity. In the ovary, some five to seven yolks grow simultaneously within small bubbles; these developing yolks comprise the 'laying series'. On the upper surface of each yolk swims a germinal disc. Once the yolk is big enough, the bubble bursts and the yellow ovum finds its way into the oviduct (a tube leading from the ovary to the uterus, or womb).

It is here that the yolk can be fertilized if mating has occurred. Male sperm, of which there may be more than one million, is stored in small glands in the oviduct. As each yolk winds its way down the oviduct, the germinal disc is fertilized by the sperm, and this will continue for 4-12 days, until all the yolks in the laying series have been fertilized. However, if mating has not occurred, the germinal disc will not be fertilized, no embryonic chick will develop and the resulting egg can be eaten.

The development of the egg now begins. As the yolk makes its way through the oviduct, it is coated with a number of layers of albumen. This is what we know as the 'white' of the egg, which is made up of water-soluble protein. As the yolk nears the end of its journey down the oviduct, it is covered with its shell membrane. When it finally reaches the uterus, it receives its calcium carbonate coating – the shell.

Of the calcium required for this, 25 per cent comes from the skeleton of the hen; the remainder has to be taken from the food she consumes. Any excess calcium in the diet is automatically deposited in the hen's bones. Finally, the shell receives an outer coating called the cuticle. This mucus layer gives the surface of the egg its colour (e.g. brown), and acts as a protective seal.

Eggs take 24 hours to develop in the hen. The laying rhythm depends on how fast the yolks mature in the ovary. Maturation, in turn, is dependent on feeding, whereas the size of the egg is determined by the age of the bird (young hens lay eggs that are approximately 20 per cent smaller than those of fully adult hens) and by the number of eggs in the series.

The more eggs in a given series, the smaller they will be since there will have been less time for the yolks to

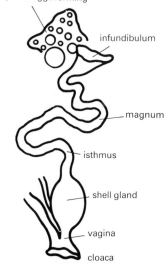

ovary with eggs forming

infundibulum

magnum

isthmus

shell gland

vagina

cloaca

The reproductive system of the hen

form and for the other stages. The first egg laid in a series is always the largest as well as the darkest in colour. Summer temperatures also have an adverse effect on the size of eggs since the hens' output is reduced at that time.

What an Egg Contains

The contents of an egg are as follows:

- albumen (the 'white'): a protein solution + mineral salts
- yolk: protein (i.e. albumen), cholesterol, lecithin (a fat emulsifier), minerals, vitamins A, B complex, D, E

An egg contains approximately:

- 74% water
- 13% albumen
- 12% fat
- 1% salts and vitamins

The fatty substance *cholesterol* is also found in eggs as it is in all other animal fats. One egg provides the daily cholesterol requirement of a fully grown human being.

good egg

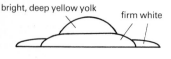

bright, deep yellow yolk

firm white

bad egg (gone stale)

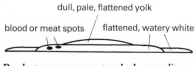

dull, pale, flattened yolk

blood or meat spots / flattened, watery white

Break open an egg as a spot check on quality

Feeding Chickens

It is of course perfectly easy to buy ready-mixed feeds (see page 60) in which case all you need do is to follow instructions from the maker or supplier.

We present here a special programme of feeding with ideas about ingredients based on the author's own experiences and allowing full scope for the most wholesome of possible care for your chickens. There is no doubt that it will provide a more varied and interesting life for both owner and chickens!

Week 1

Newborn chicks should be fed every two hours, i.e. six times a day. The following are suitable: wheat bran, rolled oats, chopped hard-boiled egg, chopped stinging nettles, plantain, dandelion and other garden greens or weeds, leftover lettuce (no sorrel as it is too acid), edible (for poultry!) calcium. A combination of any of these should be mixed together with whey (or if necessary, skimmed milk or skimmed milk powder plus water) to produce a thick crumbly mash.

One teaspoonful of yeast flakes per day may be shared between 20 chicks. It is also recommended that whey be alternated with buttermilk. One hard-boiled egg will be sufficient for four chicks each day in the first week.

If at all possible, use organically produced wheat bran; otherwise, these outer husks of wheat grain will contain too many harmful substances. Edible calcium for poultry and yeast (flakes) can be obtained

Chopped-up boiled egg is a good feed for baby chicks

from agricultural suppliers. Only buy small packs because the vitamin content decreases with age. Follow the feeding instructions.

The quantity of the mash to be given should be the amount that can be pecked up in 15 minutes. But be careful: soft or mushy food goes off quickly in summer, and this can then result in diarrhoea. Soft, mushy food must therefore always be prepared fresh!

Every other day (as a protection against worms) and daily if you wish, just as a mineral supplement, give grated carrot and crushed garlic, mixed with curds. The quantities should be 1 clove of garlic to 250 g (8¾ oz) of curds and 25 g (1 oz) of carrots to 250 g of curds. Sand and water seem to be specially needed for the chicks to be able to consume this mixture.

Week 2

Feed five times daily. Now one egg a day will be enough for six chicks. Rolled oats may now be given alone, in dry form, as a meal. Greens should no longer be so finely chopped. Seed-corn may now be given in the evenings. Carrot/garlic/curds should now only be given once every three days. Feed fruit and vegetable leftovers to the chicks.

Week 3 to 4

Feed four times a day. One egg will now be sufficient for eight chicks each day. Steamed potatoes, and artichokes for variety, if you wish, may now be added to the diet. Instead of the calcium that has been used until now, you can now give the chicks crushed egg shell that has been boiled to sterilize it; this should be available at all times alongside the sand and small stones. Give the chicks the curd mix only once a week now.

From Week 4, the chicks can look for their own greens in the run. If there is not sufficient in the run, a

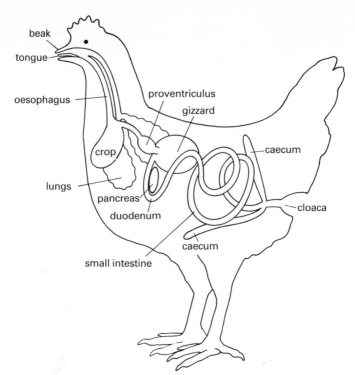

Digestive and respiratory system of the domestic fowl

wire basket containing additional greens can be hung up for the chicks to peck at. Still give seed-corn in the evenings. If the number of worms available naturally in the run is low, these may be supplemented (compost worms are easy to obtain).

Weeks 5 to 8

Feed three times a day, but give a smaller amount of rolled oats. Feed dry cereal scraps (50% wheat, 25% maize and 25% barley). In the evening, give the chicks grain and finely ground maize in the following ratio: 50% wheat, 25% barley, 25% ground maize.

From Week 8

From Week 8 feed twice daily. In the morning, let the birds look for their own food in the run. If possible, open the pop-hole shortly before sunrise when insects, worms and other life forms are easier to find in the earth (two hours later, they will have started making their way down to lower strata in the soil).

Start giving soft food – e.g. steamed potatoes or artichokes, finely minced kitchen leftovers (meat and fish without bones) – but it must be fresh and not too highly seasoned. To be on the safe side, kitchen scraps should be cooked for a short while to destroy any bacteria or mould. Finely crumbled stale bread is also very acceptable, though it, too, must be free from mould.

Stale bread can often be obtained cheaply or for nothing from a bakery. Whey may be obtainable from cheese factories or farmhouse cheesemakers.

Fruit and vegetable leftovers can be given throughout the day in the run (use windfalls!). In the evenings, give the chicks a grain mixture made up from 50% wheat, 25% barley and 25% maize, possibly ground.

The following should also be on offer throughout the day: sterilized, crushed egg shell or oystershell (which can be obtained from the agricultural merchants), sand, grit, fairly cool, clean water.

During the moulting season in autumn, sunflower seeds make a good substitute food, although hens tend to find the husks difficult. They should therefore be given shelled or mashed.

If the chickens do not show signs of starting to moult in autumn, a diet low in nutrients can be given for a week. This will usually encourage moulting to start. After moulting, egg shells are often much thicker since the rest from laying has a rejuvenating effect.

Due to the shortage of natural food in the run in winter, some form of soft food should be given in the morning.

Young hens should be given garlic water two to four times a year. This is made by finely chopping garlic cloves, adding them to water, bringing it to the boil and leaving it to simmer for a day. Depending on the freshness of the garlic, between 5 to 10 cloves should be used for every 2 litres (3½ pints) of water. When cool, this should be given instead of the normal drinking water. This prevents certain types of disease and enhances laying output. There is no need to fear that the eggs will taste of garlic. No

Always make sure that your hens have a supply of water available . . .

. . . even in the snow

other water should be available when the garlic water is given; otherwise it will be rejected in favour of the ordinary water.

During the day, in order to avoid boredom (particularly when the birds are kept primarily in hen-houses), a string bag can be hung on the wall close to the ground (but be careful about projecting nails!). This can be filled with potatoes, sugar-beet, vegetable leftovers and, if available, marrow-stalk cabbage, all of which the birds will happily peck at. (Hanging sugar-beet on nails is dangerous because the nails can easily cause injury.) Leafy vegetables and a couple of sweetcorn heads can also be scattered over the straw on the floor. The dust-bath (sand mixed with wood ash) should be kept in the hen-house in winter so as to prevent the sand from freezing.

A small, protected compost heap by the hen-house will also provide the hens with worms in winter. The space beneath the manure board can be put to good use (when not needed for the introduction of younger birds to the flock) by spreading some of the partially rotted compost there. So that it is not spread throughout the hen-house, you may be able to fix a 20 cm (8 in) high board where it will retain it.

Seed-corn

This has a considerably higher nutritional value than ordinary grain, not only because the nutrients are more readily assimilated, but because the vitamin content during germination is greatly increased.

Two styles of feeder to cater for a flock of chickens. Ready-mixed compound feeds can cut down on work if you want to save the time

To prepare, soak wheat, oats, barley and maize seeds in water for a day and then spread out in boxes. If foil or uncoloured cloth is put in the bottom, this will help to keep in the moisture which must be maintained for four to five days in order for germination to take place.

After this time, the grains are about 1-2 cm (⅜-¾ in) long, and the corn can be fed to the birds as it is. Because

59

grain goes off quite quickly after germination, it is a good idea to place a quantity of corn in boxes for germination each day to maintain a constant supply.

If it is not possible to obtain the organically grown product, maize should be used sparingly because this cereal usually receives a great deal of chemical treatment.

Ready-mixed Feeds

You can buy different varieties for specific purposes: chick feed, pullet rearing feed, laying hen meal or pellets (dry food pressed into small cylindrical pieces). These ready-mixed feeds can cut down on work and ensure that birds get the nutrients they need.

However, this type of feed is not cheap, and a hen will consume approximately 120 g (4½ oz) a day – i.e. 40-45 kg (90-100 lb) annually. Maintaining a good run will save you around one third of this food requirement. In addition, we are thinking in terms of poultry-keeping as a hobby or for self-sufficiency, and for this, you should always try to keep things as natural as possible.

If you are prepared to go to the expense of ready-mixed feed, it is debatable whether you might just as well go to the supermarket for eggs and meat, since the birds sold there will have been fed in this way. Ready-mixed feeds contain just those questionable chemicals and additives that people often strive to remove from their diets, but which are an essential part of large-scale poultry-rearing.

It is also a good idea to avoid feeding your chickens bone meal, blood meal, animal- and fish-product meal. Although these have a high protein content, they also contain the remains of the solvent *perchlorethylene*, which is required for their production. You could also happily do without the yolk colouring agent added to the feed designed for laying hens.

If, on the other hand, you are on friendly terms with a butcher, you can have him provide you with freshly ground bone meal; in addition to protein, this will contain many minerals and phosphoric acid.

Careful thought must also be given to the widely acclaimed 'rich in protein' soya bean. In the first place, we get soya beans from Third World countries whose ecology is suffering under this monoculture. Secondly, these crops are extensively sprayed with dangerous insecticides, the use of which is forbidden in Europe.

Feeding your Hens during a Short Period of Absence

If you are going away for the weekend, you must leave your chickens enough water, grain and seeds to last for two days. Place these, in separate containers, in the hen-house. With few exceptions, birds will only eat as much as they need.

It will also be helpful if you can find a neighbour who will open the pop-hole in the morning and shut it up again at night. You must never underestimate the possibility of predators finding their way in at night. After very cold and wet nights, or when some of the hens have got into the

Free-range chickens hunting

habit of 'mislaying' their eggs (e.g. somewhere in the run), the pop-hole should not be opened until late morning.

Housing Chickens

The essential order to follow when keeping animals is: first the housing, then the animals! Those who make do with temporary housing at the start are doing neither themselves nor their animals a favour. The daily work will be more difficult to carry out, and the birds will become unwell and out of sorts; in addition, neighbours will tend to voice their disapproval. It is therefore important to follow this sequence:

1 How do your neighbours feel about you keeping chickens? Perhaps they would like an egg or two, or the occasional chicken?
2 Find out if the local authority actually permits poultry-keeping in your area. If the answer is yes, make your application for planning permission to put up the hen-house.
3 Once planning permission has been granted, the work can start:
   a Strip off the topsoil from the chicken-house area.
   b Dig trenches for foundations to support the walls.
   c Fill trenches with concrete.
   d Cover floor area with gravel and cover with a thick layer of sand and then a layer of clinker.

e Make provision for a drainage slope, preferably towards the south.

4 The housing itself can now be built, either from hollow blocks (which will then need to be plastered) or from double wooden walls. Small hen-houses should be square, whereas larger ones should be rectangular.

There must be sufficient space in the hen-house, particularly in winter when the birds are kept inside all day. At that time of year, feeding troughs and drinkers (both standing on bricks to prevent contamination from the straw, and to prevent water freezing), as well as sand and grit containers (oystershell or egg shell) will have to be indoors, and you will still have to ensure that the hens have enough

space to scratch around. There should, in addition, be a box for partially rotted compost in the house so that worms and other grubs can be scratched for during the cold months.

When you are considering how big to build your hen-house, a useful guideline is two hens per square metre (10 sq ft). It is, however, better to have too much space than too little. If the hen-house is to be incorporated with housing for other animals, it is important to remember that hens and pigs should be housed as far as possible from one another because hens can infect pigs with disease.

It is also desirable to have water and power supplies in the hen-house. And finally an infra-red lamp is important, especially in winter and for chicks without a broody hen.

Alternative Building Materials

If wood is used, it should not be chemically treated; try rendering it

Portable housing for use in paddocks or large gardens

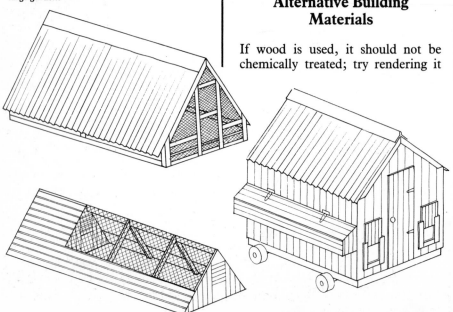

Inside a small chicken-house

Pop-hole conference outside a small chicken-house

with ordinary wood ash (there are wood-ash-treated hen-houses in some parts of the Black Forest in West Germany which are over 100 years old).

In some countries people use clay as a building material. After all, it is sound and distributes temperature evenly. However, it is not perfectly suited for hen-houses, particularly as a floor material, because, in the event of sickness among the birds, you will have to remove the floor up to a depth of at least 30 cm (12 in).

There is also the problem that clay can be penetrated by mice, rats or weasels, so that if you do want a clay hen-house, you should at the least install a layer of wire netting in the ground for protection. Lastly, clay walls will eventually develop holes since the hens peck at them.

The Roof

A lean-to roof can easily be made by an amateur, whereas a ridge-roof will require more expertise. For insulation, chicken-keepers in some areas cover the hen-house with turf, which keeps in the warmth in winter, and will keep out excessive heat in summer.

The roof should protrude over the walls far enough to prevent rain from soaking the window frames. Ideally, the eves of the roof should dip downwards a little.

The Floor

A cement-based floor will be very cold, and it will only be possible to make it suitably warm if you cover it with a very thick layer of straw (at least 30 cm/12 in). Wooden floors will need protection against mice – i.e. a layer of thin wire mesh underground. In addition, because of the wet droppings and the six-monthly hosing down, a wooden floor will not last for long.

Windows

These should face the south or southeast so that the sun's rays fall on and dry the floor of the hen-house: major diseases can be caused by damp, draughty conditions. To provide ventilation, one imaginative way is to fix small, removable glass panels in the walls adjacent to the window wall, immediately beneath the roof.

Fresh air is usually provided through outward-opening windows, which should be as large as possible.

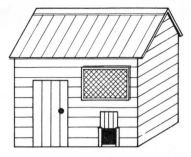

Limited land calls for static housing: (above) a garden poultry shed in hen run; (below) a veranda unit

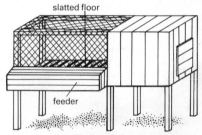

slatted floor

feeder

manure collects below

'Industrial-style' battery cages

If the window opens inwards, the hens will always sit on top of it and defecate over the panes, so that, before long, light will no longer be able to get through. Even sash windows are more use than that.

The opening of all windows should be made safe against predators, *and* against the hens using it as a door, by covering it with horizontal wooden bars and chicken wire.

Glass panels that are not pulled open to provide ventilation can act as additional sources of light on the west and east sides of the house. In the case of smaller hen-houses, the door can also serve as the window.

The Doorway or Pop-hole

A board should be nailed across the bottom of the doorway up to a height of 10-20 cm/4-10 in (depending on the depth of straw) so that, when the door is opened, not too much straw will be pulled out. It must be possible to fasten the door in its open position.

In small hen-houses, the entrance is just large enough to allow a chicken through – this is known as a pop-hole.

With larger houses, serious thought should be given to having a door and passageway that are wide enough to allow a wheelbarrow to pass through. The way into and out of the hen-house should be protected from the wind by a porch, with doors or flaps opening outwards to either side known as a 'pop-hole protector' in the smaller houses.

The heavier breeds have particular trouble negotiating raised gang-planks, but other birds, especially young ones, have problems with them, too. It is best, therefore, for the entrance to be at ground level. It

Small ark for keeping chickens on the lawn

Pop-hole peepers

Nest-boxes are often built to allow outside egg collection

Inside view of the same nest-box

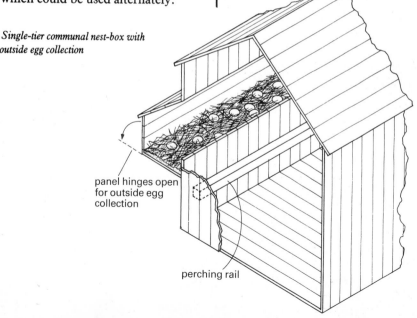

pop-hole closing slide

pop-hole

entrance to 'porch'

A pop-hole protector or small porch to keep out draughts

should also be on the same side as the window to prevent through-draughts. If possible, there should be two ways in and out of the hen-house, which could be used alternately.

Single-tier communal nest-box with outside egg collection

panel hinges open for outside egg collection

perching rail

Nest Boxes

The best position for the nest boxes is on the south side by the window so that they will be in half-light. One nest box should be provided for every two to three hens. Each box should have a sloping roof (or it will become too densely coated with bird droppings) and a perch on one side for the birds to fly up to.

The nest boxes should contain frequently changed straw and a china or plaster egg, because nests in which there is already one egg have a greater attraction for hens than empty nests. Boxes should not be more than 1 m (3¼ ft) from ground level, or 20 cm (8 in) at the most in the case of 'non-flying' breeds.

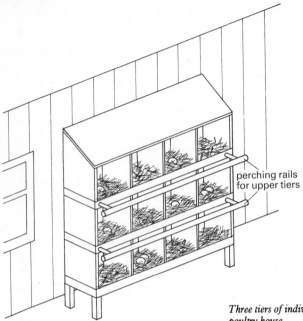

Three tiers of individual nest-boxes inside a larger poultry house

Shared nest boxes are also quite common and are acceptable to hens even though this means that they have to find their way across already laid eggs, which can result in eggs being cracked. A shared nest box measuring 1 × 1 m (3¼ × 3¼ ft) will be sufficient for 5 hens.

Perches

These should be made of 5 × 5 cm (2 × 2 in) timber and should not be longer than 2 m (6½ ft); otherwise they become too awkward to clean. The undersides must be planed and rubbed down to a smooth finish so that germs cannot infiltrate the wood. Finally, they should be treated with wood ash. From time to time, the undersides can be smeared with soft soap. The perches should be removed twice a year for cleaning: scrub with soft soap and water, and leave them in the sun to dry.

Manure Board

A manure, or droppings, board should be placed on a slant beneath the perches. As well as its obvious purpose, the board will also provide space beneath the perches for the hens to walk around or for the introduction of young birds to the flock.

Before the hen-house is used for the first time, sawdust or sand should be spread over the board to prevent the birds coming into contact with their droppings, and to facilitate the once-a-week removal of the droppings. Scatter more sawdust or sand over the manure board each day so that the watery element of the manure is

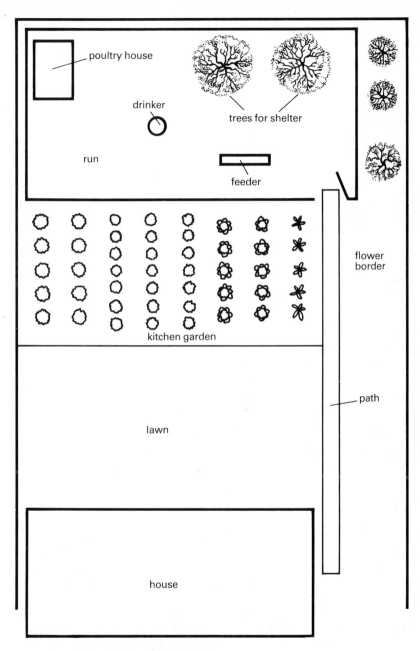

poultry house

drinker

trees for shelter

run

feeder

flower border

kitchen garden

path

lawn

house

A typical back-garden poultry enterprise

71

absorbed; this will also help prevent ammonia vapour, which would attract vermin and pollute the air.

Sometimes a deep-pit system incorporating a chicken-wire covering is used under the perches. However, the wire is difficult to clean, and there is always a build-up of ammonia vapour, even when the sun does not shine directly into the pit.

The Run

Ten hens and one cock will need a run with an area of between 150 and 200 sq m (1600-2100 sq ft). It should be fenced in to a height of between 1.5 and 2.5 m (5-8 ft) depending on the type of hen. If birds are to treat fences with respect, the lower part must be made from fine-mesh chicken wire.

It is very important that bushes, hedges, espalier fruit bushes, etc., divide up the run into several areas: these provide shelter and variety. However, flower borders and vegetable beds would be destroyed by the chickens within a few days.

If the run does contain its own flourishing shrubbery, this will provide hens with an additional source of food, both in terms of the insects that will be attracted and the ripe berries in autumn (blackberries, raspberries, hips, etc.). A few weeks before the hens take up occupancy, a wild-seed mix (which can be obtained from agricultural suppliers) should be sown; this is because ordinary grass is not sufficient for pasture.

Ideally, there should be deciduous trees in front of the window side of the hen-house: these will provide shade in summer and let the sun through in winter. Around the doorway, it is a good idea to spread gravel because the hens' scratching will soon eradicate any grass from that area. Where this has begun to happen, food should only be put down occasionally, and that area should be left unmown.

If there is a compost heap in the run, it will be a popular target for the hens, and if it is not properly secured, it will end up all over the run. What is needed is something like a slatted box around 50 cm (20 in) high in which a small quantity of partially rotted compost is spread. The hens are then free to do their worst, and the compost will soon be enriched with hen droppings.

A covered box will act as a dust-bath – ideally positioned so that it is in the shade. Wood ash can be mixed in with the sand to help control pests.

GEESE

The greylag goose is the main wild 'ancestor' of most breeds of domesticated geese, while the swan goose of Asia is the ancestor of the breed we know as the Chinese goose.

Elsewhere in the world the Egyptian goose (wild) has probably contributed to the formation of some domestic breeds.

Geese were kept as domestic animals as long ago as 3000 to 4000 BC. The Greeks considered them symbols of fertility, and the Romans used them as 'watch-dogs' after one occasion when they raised the alarm during a nocturnal attack on the Roman capital by the Gauls.

Over this long period, the domestic goose has only retained traces of the behaviour patterns of the wild bird, even though its external appearance has changed little. So it has come about that their former reputation as wise geese has now given way to the term 'silly goose', attributable mainly to their incorrigible stubbornness and their inflexibility.

Greylag geese – closely related to domestic geese

Giving ready-mixed feed for geese and ducks

Characteristics and Behaviour

Although wild and domestic geese differ a great deal in their behaviour, they do remain quite alike physically. In addition, they have enough behavioural characteristics in common to make a brief description of the greylag goose worthwhile. This goose has been chosen because its behaviour characteristics were studied in depth by Konrad Lorenz, the pioneer Austrian ethologist. His very readable and entertaining book *Das Jahr* *der Graugans* (Year of the Greylag Goose) gives a more detailed account.

Geese are grazing and water birds. (Greylag geese, in addition, are flying birds, covering many hundreds of miles a year.) They are exclusively vegetarian, their beaks being suited to both grazing and pecking up grain, as well as to gnawing fruit, vegetables and other scraps of food. They prefer to eat sweet, tender grasses which, together with a good quantity of grit (an ample supply of which they swallow before going out to graze in the morning), finds its way down into the bird's crop.

Smell, taste and touch

Their sense of smell and taste is somewhat more developed than the domestic chicken's but they are alike in that their sense of touch is the most highly developed. When they want to smell something, this is usually accompanied by a shaking of the head.

Vision and hearing

With their sharp eyes, positioned for long-range vision, geese can see distant objects very well, and their long necks enhance this ability. They prefer open pasture land: they are not at all keen on overgrown borders where vision is obstructed, nor do they like walking along unfamiliar paths where they cannot see over hedges.

Domestic geese also react immediately to the slightest change in their environment. For instance, they will emphatically refuse to enter their housing if there happens to be a bucket near it which is not usually there.

Their sense of hearing is as developed as that of owls, the most sharp-eared of all wild birds.

Body temperature

As with chickens, their body temperature is around 40-43°C (104-109.4°F). Whereas goslings need the warmth of their mothers to survive, heating is shunned by young birds at five to six weeks as their feathers slowly develop. Adult geese seem quite impervious to cold.

Vocalization

The goose does not have the same range of significant vocal sounds as the chicken does. However, vocal contact is just as important for them in their lives together.

The gosling will already have established contact with the mother bird while still in the egg. If the egg happens to cool down or is not lying properly in the nest, the gosling will emit a repeated cheeping sound as a distress signal. If everything is put right and the mother answers its call, it will then 'greet' her, as Lorenz puts it, with a series of double cheeping sounds.

Goslings are also in contact with one another during the hatching process, though not so markedly as with chicks. During hatching, vocal contact between goslings and goose prevents the latter from gnawing at the edges of the egg shell, which she would otherwise be eager to do.

Goslings are 'nest-fleers' (nidifuges): they can run about surprisingly soon after hatching. During their very first moments after hatching, they are a little weak and bedraggled, but after only a few minutes they start to react to their mother's voice by raising their heads high and craning their necks. This is when their first 'wi' sounds of greeting are heard.

At about five to six weeks, when their outline feathers are growing, the goslings find their voices, and the 'wi' sounds become a cackle. Both of these sounds, when accompanied by a forward extension of the head, serve as a greeting. When the head is not in

75

this position, the sounds simply maintain vocal contact within the group – what might be called common babbling, and used to communicate a happy corporate identity.

In order to make threatening sounds, geese raise their heads, stretch out their necks as far forward as they can, fix their opponents with their eyes, emit a loud hissing sound and beat their wings. If one party decides to give in, it lowers its head, pulls in its neck, averts its eyes and tries to turn to the side.

The Gander

In the greylag goose, the gander makes a well-timed appearance just after the eggs have hatched. Before then, he limited himself to watching the nest from a distance so as not to betray its location. Now, however, his presence is important because, within a few hours, the goslings will make their first excursion with the mother bird and the gander's job will be to protect the family from predators.

It is also imperative that the goslings get to know him now because they are at the 'imprinting' stage already referred to in connection with chickens. This impressionable stage is even more pronounced in wild geese than in domestic ones. Whoever first makes contact with the goslings, such that their voice and appearance are imprinted on the minds of the goslings, will always be regarded as a protector and a place of refuge.

The goose and gander will always be on the same level in the order of precedence. Their readiness to

Male and female geese look alike to us: gander (left), goose (right)

defend their family and their aggressiveness increase with the number of goslings, although the gander will be more prepared to attack than the female. However, a goose without a gander will hardly, if ever, defend her goslings. It can sometimes happen, therefore, that an unpaired gander will 'adopt' fatherless goslings and bring them up together with the goose.

Keep off my wife!

76

A flock of geese is usually led by one gander – the largest and strongest in the flock. Once he has attained it, he does not need to fight to maintain his position as leader. Only at the mating season is it possible for changes to occur.

Early Life

Shortly after hatching, goslings lose their wet appearance as the horny sheaths surrounding their feathers are loosened. To the human eye, ganders and geese are very difficult to distinguish, although the gander's voice tends to be higher in pitch.

No sooner have they learned how to walk, they begin looking for food. The yolk sac which they ingested just before hatching will give them enough nourishment for the first two days, of course, but they still need to learn – from their parents and by trial and error – what is edible and what is not.

Goslings often make tugging movements at this time, grasping everything in reach with their beaks. These hefty tugs often cause them to lose their balance and fall over.

When the goslings want to get warm, they slide under their mother's feathers from behind, making a gentle trilling sound – the so-called 'sleeping sound'. This rubbing against the goose's feathers has another purpose: goose down is impervious to water because, when the goslings rub against their mother, they become electrostatically charged, thus repelling water. (Later, when their real feathers grow at five or six months, they will grease them with fat from their rump glands, spreading this over their bodies with their neck, head and beak.)

After only two to four days, the family will be making extensive excursions to, if at all possible, ponds or brooks because water offers them refuge from predators. It is now that the importance of the imprinting stage is revealed for the goslings will follow their parents unconditionally wherever they go.

Within 12 days of hatching, rivalry develops among the young ganders, who display the same behavioural patterns as fully grown males. The parents remain passive during this scuffling, merely providing refuge for those who lose fights. The battle for order of precedence is then suspended until the geese reach sexual maturity.

The goslings very quickly gain independence and are soon taking the lead on excursions. They will, for instance, exhibit marked opposition to leaving a place they find agreeable, and will continue to cry or whine about it until the parent birds give in. In the presence of enemies – and these may simply be one or two other families of geese approaching the goslings' family's territory – birds as young as three days will join their parents' hissing and threatening sounds. At this age, they will also quite independently take up their places in the order of precedence within the flock.

Unpaired family members – e.g. brothers or sisters of the parents –

Wild geese have impressive powers of flight and orientation (these are Greenland whitefronts) often join in with a family that contains goslings and help the parents to defend the young from predators. In a threatening situation, several families may join together: the adults will encircle the goslings and then hiss, shriek and beat their wings to ward off the enemy. This can be very effective, even against larger predators. Domestic geese too – and ganders in particular – will attack enemies, especially when there are goslings. The more the goslings grow, the more the individual families reintegrate with the rest of the flock.

The goslings soon learn the daily routine. Every day a thorough bath is taken. Swimming geese immerse their necks deep in the water, then lean back and let the water run down their backs. They also dive and beat their wings. Then, back on the land, they meticulously preen their feathers, stretch their legs and wings and, after a short while, settle down to their midday nap, accompanying this with a gentle chattering sound.

Flying

When the goslings are about five to six weeks old, the parent birds go into a second moult and lose their power of flight. However, by the time the young are ready to fly, at the age of eight to ten weeks (at ten weeks, feather growth comes to an end and the wing tips then cross over the back), the parents' pinions (flight feathers) will have grown back. They are then able to accompany their offspring in their early flights, because the young birds will not yet have the necessary experience.

Domestic geese, particularly the lighter breeds and young birds, also enjoy flying, although they do not fly as high or for as long as greylags. In the morning after sunrise, when the goose's day begins, they like to fly a lap of honour around their pasture, and they do the same just before returning home in the evening. Old geese and heavy breeds are no longer able to do this, however.

Geese have a very good sense of direction. Flying birds cannot survive without this ability, but even domestic geese quickly learn where their pasture is, and if they are taken away by their human keepers, they are able to find their way back over considerable distances. In the evening, they return home by themselves – especially if some oats (their favourite cereal) are waiting for them. In the autumn, wild geese migrate, engaging in large-scale formation flying.

Courtship and Mating

The goose is capable of reproduction when she is one year old, although fertilization, brooding and rearing are more successful with older birds.

In spring, the mating season starts. A young wild gander of at least two years of age will choose a young goose of another family (pairing always occurs outside of the family in the case of wild geese). First, he courts her from a distance, making continuous calling sounds while, at the same time, adopting an unusual body position: he holds his neck in an s-shaped curve in front of his body. The female, still living with her family at this point, behaves very shyly.

After a while, however, the gander plucks up more courage, draws closer and does all he can to look conspicuous. He flies up and down in front of her, performs overacted take-off and landing manoeuvres and fends off those who are not involved. After winning the battle, he returns to the goose with loud cries of triumph and hopes for her consent. To begin with – if she finds him to her liking – she will only chatter back quietly. However, if she later joins in with his cries of triumph, the two birds are regarded as a pair. This pairing will then last for life.

The pairing behaviour of domestic geese, on the other hand, differs greatly from that of their wild cousins. Monogamy is no longer the usual pattern – in fact, each gander will usually pair with three to five females. However, it is known that the gander will prefer one goose in particular, the eggs of the others remaining unfertilized. (Whether flocks still contain family groupings remains to be ascertained.)

In general, when geese are kept domestically, sexual activity takes place throughout the year, with the result that mating plays a far more

Wild geese pair up for life (these are greater snow geese)

Left: *Buff Laced Wyandotte Bantam hen*
Below left: *Modern Game Bantam – Red-black cockerel*
Below right: *Black Minorca Bantam cock*

82

Gold Sebright hen
A pair of Sebrights (Sebrights are all Bantams)

Silver Sebright hen

important role in their communal life. Pre-mating behaviour, on the other hand, is only recognizable in parts.

The domestic gander begins his courting with the same display of impressive behaviour as a wild gander, to which the goose responds with interest. He then brings her a piece of food, as a token gesture, and the goose raises herself a little from the ground. Both birds move their necks increasingly faster until, standing side by side, they lay their necks across one another's shoulders, their bills making their way through the feathers, and at the same time move round in a circle. Finally, the female lowers herself and the gander mounts her, keeping a tight grip on her head with his bill.

In the water, mating is triggered by a dipping of the bill in the water. While this is going on, the rest of the geese stand or swim around making a chattering sound. Occasionally, some of the other geese may try to join in during mating, and the females may partially mount one another in the excitement.

Domestic geese can live as long as 40 years. Since geese mourn and pine when they lose their partner or family, it is very important that all the birds, apart from the breeding stock, be killed at more or less the same time.

Nesting and Brooding

The gander is able to fertilize a goose when 12-14 months old, and at 280 to 300 days the goose begins to lay eggs. Throughout her life, a wild goose will lay 20 to 60 eggs on average, but a domestic goose, with laying periods in spring and in autumn, will have a higher output. However, it is difficult to rear goslings born in the autumn, and the goose's laying capacity in the next spring will suffer.

The nesting and brooding behaviour of the domestic goose is still quite similar to that of the wild goose. Shortly before she is about to lay, the goose builds up nesting material around herself, and often builds on to the nest during brooding, lining it with feathers pulled out of her front.

When the goose leaves the nest to look for food, defecate, drink and bathe, she first carefully covers the nest with nest material. Since the eggs need to be moistened several times a day, and this is most easily accomplished by the wet feathers of the goose, it is very important that there be some facility for bathing.

When she returns to the nest, the goose carefully rolls the eggs back under her body using her bill. It is important to ensure, in the case of the domestic goose, that the eggs are actually cooled, moistened and rolled several times a day. In her domesticated state, she may tend to overlook this part of her 'duty'.

Breeds and Buying

There are only a few breeds of geese, the main difference being their weight, which has an effect on their capacity for brooding and rearing goslings. It would be most sensible if we look at the types which have developed in different parts of Europe.

The Toulouse Goose

The greyish brown or greyish blue Toulouse goose from France was reared as long ago as the 14th century, primarily for liver pâté. Because of the discomfort that this type of rearing and forced feeding causes the bird, cramming is now prohibited in many countries including Britain.

Owing to their massive body structure, which prevents them from walking, these geese are not suited to grazing. Nor is it easy to sell this type of goose since most poultry-keepers have no wish for a giant goose with heavy bones which, because of its high food consumption, must carry a correspondingly high price. Nevertheless the Toulouse goose does give an abundant supply of feathers.

A typical feature of the Toulouse goose is the feathered dewlap and a paunch which may hang down to the ground. Goose fanciers pay high prices for goslings and older birds since the stately appearance of the latter can be quite impressive.

There are divergent views on the reliability of Toulouse geese for brooding. This, of course, depends on the age of the birds concerned, since they are not fully grown until they are two years old. So for breeding purposes only fully grown birds (both geese and ganders) should be used.

It is also best, with this breed, to put only one goose and one gander together because the gander, due to his large body size, finds mating difficult – in fact, deep water is essential if it is to take place at all. The gander weighs approximately 10 to 15 kg (22-33 lb) and the goose 9 to 12 kg (20-26½ lb), laying up to 40 eggs of around 200 g (7 oz).

The Embden Goose

The white Embden goose, often crossed with the Toulouse, was originally from East Friesland on the Dutch/German border, and is also a very heavy goose. Brooding and rearing are difficult because the Embden has almost completely lost these instincts, despite the fact that, during her lifetime, the female lays up to 70 eggs weighing about 170 g (6 oz) each.

Because of their great weight, the same problems are experienced with selling and mating as with the Toulouse goose: the gander weighs approximately 11 to 12 kg (25-27 lb) and the goose 10 to 11 kg (22-25 lb).

Only the male goslings are pure white in colour, the females having variegated grey feathers. By the time they are one year old they are all pure white. The white colour is the result of selective breeding.

The Pomeranian Goose

The pure white, variegated or grey Pomeranian goose is also classed as a heavy breed, though in this case, the gander weighs only around 7 to 8 kg (15½-17¾ lb) and the female 5 to 7 kg (11-15½ lb). Typical of this breed are the good meat deposits on the breast and legs, which are smoked and sold as a delicacy.

Because little cross-breeding has taken place, this breed has retained good brooding and rearing instincts,

Embden geese
Sebastopol geese

Toulouse geese

and the goslings are fairly resistant to unfavourable weather conditions. Moreover, the goose broods comparatively late in the spring which also facilitates rearing. She will hatch two sets of 10-15 or more eggs, the average weight being 180 g (6¼ oz) per egg. This breed is popular in Germany and neighbouring countries.

The Roman Goose

The Roman was introduced in Britain early this century, and in subsequent importations. Today the breed is pure white. It is active, alert, graceful and docile in character, with a compact plump body and a deep, broad outline. It has a high proportion of meat to bone and offal. Adult birds weigh between 4.5 and 6.3 kg (10-14 lb).

The Sebastopol Goose

This goose comes from south-east Europe. Its feathers, particularly those on its back, are curly or frizzled and some can be so long that they trail on the ground. This breed is kept mainly by goose fanciers since rearing the goslings is very demanding because of the slow development of their feathers. Adult birds weigh between 4 and 5 kg (8¾-11 lb).

The Chinese Goose

This goose – also known as the 'humped' goose – has its natural habitat in Siberia, China and Japan, and came to Europe in the 18th century. It is distinguished by the protuberance on its forehead, which grows with age, and the greyish brown streaks running from the head down the back.

Chinese geese weigh between 4 and 6 kg (8¾-13 lb), and are good agile grazers. The goose lays two sets of 15 eggs (total output can be up to 80 eggs) and is a reliable brooder. Goslings are very hardy. The meat quality of this breed is highly praised.

Brooding and Rearing

A breeding pair should be at least two years old, or three years old in the case of heavy breeds. Breeding females should be replaced after eight to ten years, and ganders after about five years. Since the birds need time to get to know one another and their new surroundings, breeding stock should be put together in the autumn. Breeding geese should be ringed so that they are not killed by mistake with the birds bred for slaughter the following autumn.

In the case of light breeds, there should be one gander to two to four geese. Depending on the breed, geese lay their eggs between February and April, and hatching takes between 28 and 32 days.

The Nest

Nests should be set up all year round in the goose house, separated from each other by a dividing wall so that each goose can lay and hatch in peace. A piece of grassy turf placed with the roots upwards in the nest serves as a springy base for a good layer of straw.

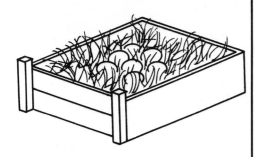

For natural incubation (for both geese and ducks), a nest can be made within a timber surround

The turf is important because, otherwise, as time goes by, the heavy weight of the goose will compress the straw and the eggs will then be lying on the ground and could be squashed.

The nest should be held together by means of a wooden frame (80 × 80 cm/32 × 32 in). A brick surround should only be used as a last resort because the geese may injure their delicate feet on the edges; the goslings can also easily fall over it when they first leave the nest after hatching, and may be unable to get back in by themselves. For this reason, you should ensure that the top half of the wooden frame at the front can be folded down.

Brooding

The first egg should be marked and then left in the nest. It will usually be unfertilized, but if there is no egg in the nest, the goose might move to another one. As further eggs are laid, they should be marked (using a pencil because the ink of felt-tipped pens is absorbed through the shell) with the date of laying and the name of the goose, and kept in a place that is cool (10-14°C/50-57.2°F) and humid (75% relative humidity). They must be turned daily. When selecting eggs for hatching, use the same advice that was given earlier for chickens.

When the goose remains on the nest for longer periods of time, and lines it with feathers plucked from her front, this is a sign that broodiness has begun. She should first be given the older eggs to sit on, followed by the rest a day later. If at all possible, the eggs should not be any older than 14 days. The goose should be given as many eggs as she can cover – between 10 and 15.

On the 9th or 10th day after the start of brooding, the eggs should be candled; it is difficult to see much before this point. Candling should then be carried out again on the 20th day.

During brooding, it is necessary to ensure that the goose actually leaves the nest several times a day, has a bath, and moistens and turns the eggs. Even if the goose is away from the nest for more than half an hour, this does not harm the eggs if they have been carefully covered with nesting material.

Inspecting your goose's clutch of eggs can be difficult if the gander is watching over the nest when the goose leaves it. The best thing to do is to lure him away with some oats. When removing eggs for candling, it is essential that the door to the housing be closed, for if the goose happens to return unexpectedly early, she will become very agitated. If, on the other hand, you return the eggs too late, it will not be possible to put them back under her because she will prevent you from approaching.

Above: *The Call duck is an ornamental breed*
Left: *Rouen drake*

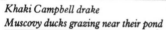

Khaki Campbell drake
Muscovy ducks grazing near their pond

Aylesbury ducks on water

Hatching

Between Days 28 and 32 – in some cases later, depending on the age of the eggs – the first eggs will crack. It may then take up to 24 hours from the first hole appearing until the gosling is hatched. On rare occasions, no progress may be made after 24 hours; then the eggs should be sprinkled with lukewarm water, which will facilitate hatching.

On no account should newly hatched goslings be removed from the mother before all the latecomers have hatched. If too few of the eggs were fertilized, this is no problem: additional goslings of the same age as the hatched ones, can be put under the goose in the evening.

The yolk sac in the goslings' stomachs provides nourishment for two days, but there must be a supply of water and somewhere to graze. It is very important that there be plenty of straw spread on the ground, although this is no easy matter because geese are always producing a large quantity of wet droppings. The best solution is

Sprinkling with lukewarm water helps to hatch goose eggs

to cover the soiled straw with a good quantity of fresh straw each evening and then remove the whole lot once a week. The corners of the housing should be rounded off or filled in, either with thick pasteboard or with straw to prevent any of the goslings being crushed in the corners. Nothing else is required when goslings are being reared by a goose.

If, however, the goslings are to be reared without a mother bird, this will require more work. The goslings should be kept for the first few days in a separate, warm and dry section of the goose house (if possible, where they will get a lot of sunlight), with yet more straw which must also be dry. The length of this period will depend on the age of the birds and on the weather. During the night, at least, the goslings should be kept warm with an infra-red lamp. Depending on the size of the birds, there should be one lamp to every 7-10 goslings.

Careful observation will show whether enough warmth is being provided. If the goslings are lying one on top of another because there is insufficient space beneath the lamp, they will be crushed. If, on the other hand, they are lying in a relaxed fashion, gently cheeping, under the lamp, everything is just right.

The following guidelines indicate the temperatures that goslings need in their housing:
Day 1 to Day 3: 30°C (86°F)
Up to Day 7: 28°C (82.4°F)
Up to Day 12: 26°C (78.8°F)
Up to Day 18: 24°C (75.2°F)
Up to Day 21: 20°C (68°F), and thereafter 18°C (64.4°F)

After the 5th and 6th week, when the feathers develop, the birds will no longer need any extra heating, except perhaps in very cold weather. They must, of course, be protected from draughts. If the goose house is quite large, bales of straw can be stacked around the gosling section and, in a cold spell, it is a good idea to place a partial covering over this section.

Since goslings will peck right from the start, baskets of greens should be hung in their housing. Otherwise, they will peck at one another's down in their boredom.

In sunny weather the goslings should be put into a large cage-like run within the main run, at a spot where there is protection from wind and where there is good ground cover. It goes without saying that the protected run must be enlarged and replaced from time to time as the birds grow.

'Foster Parents'

It is not really a good idea to use broody hens, turkeys or ducks to hatch goose eggs. Although this is sometimes practised, it brings with it a host of added complications:

- Neither chickens nor turkeys moisten their eggs.
- The broody hen is often unable to turn the eggs properly because they are too heavy for her.
- The incubation period of goose eggs is longer than for chickens' and turkeys' eggs.
- Goose eggs need to be cooled several times a day and for longer periods than the eggs of other birds.

- Ducks often make far less reliable broodies than geese.

There will also be problems with rearing because of the different behaviour patterns of the birds:

- Broody hens become agitated when goslings want to go into the water. Turkeys also want nothing to do with water. Geese, on the other hand, deliberately choose the water's edge for rearing their young.
- Chickens, turkeys and ducks are not wholly vegetarian as geese are, and since goslings take their cue from the assumed parent bird, they will become very confused.
- Broody hens will want to avoid open land, whereas the goslings will look for pasture where vision is not obstructed.
- The very intense imprinting behaviour that goslings exhibit towards their 'mother' may lead to inappropriate characteristics being learned, which will confuse the geese for the rest of their lives.
- The body language and vocal sounds of the different birds, not to mention their social behaviour, differ greatly.

So if you have a pair of geese that are not very reliable for brooding purposes, it is far better to have the eggs hatched at a hatchery, and then have the goslings returned for the true parents to rear. Geese will frequently adopt goslings, even if they are of a different breed and not newly hatched, since they always organize themselves into family groups.

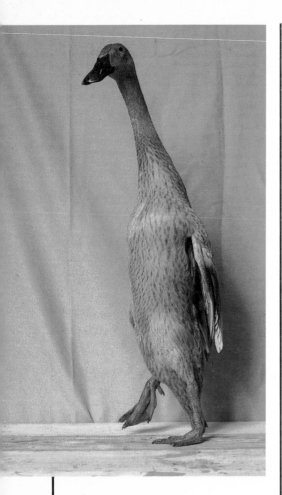

Above: *Indian Runner duck*
Top right: *White Indian Runner flock*
Right: *Indian Runner drake*

Bronze turkey pair
Crollwitzer Stag turkey

Broad-breasted White turkeys

Geese are exclusively vegetarians: these have been provided with turf for grazing

Feeding Geese

As with chickens, proprietary feeds are available ready-made for geese, which are very easy to use. Again, we present here an alternative which, while probably saving you a certain amount of cash, is also entirely natural and therefore more satisfying. During the first week, the goslings will be very slow eaters. You should only put down the amount of food that will be eaten within 10 to 15 minutes, ensuring that each bird is able to eat during that period. In the first week, food is given on flat plates.

Water containers should be deep enough for the goslings to be able to immerse their heads, otherwise they may develop eye infections. On the other hand, they should be prevented from standing in the drinkers; otherwise, they will soon dirty the water and spread it over the straw. You should therefore place a large flowerpot (upside down) or a large stone in the water dispenser.

Better still, a special turned-up drinker can be bought from farm suppliers. This drinker should be placed on bricks so that no straw will get into it and the birds will not be able to defecate in it. However, it must not be so high that the goslings are unable to dip their heads in the water.

The food intended for goslings should be inaccessible to the older birds. Soft food will cover the goslings' bills and nostrils, so it is best not to give them this during the first few weeks. If you do, a considerable amount of the food would end up in the drinking water and go off, and the rest of it will be smeared over the young birds' down where it will harden. The other goslings will peck at this until the bare skin is exposed.

Between May and end November (when it is ready for killing), a gosling will eat around 10 kg (22 lb) of corn if there is sufficient grazing land available. As a rule, a young goose will be ready for slaughter by ten weeks if fed on oats and potatoes.

Between Weeks 5 and 9, the gosling puts on around 80 g (2½ oz) a day, after which its growth rate falls to 15 g (½ oz) a day until Week 12. It is only when the birds reach sexual maturity that their weight begins to increase at a higher rate. At the age of 10 to 12 weeks, goose meat is very low in fat, but unfortunately, there are few buyers at this time of year (July).

When bad weather keeps the young birds from grazing, baskets of greens, lettuce or other tender vegetables as well as windfalls should be hung in their housing at head height. This is also a good idea for relieving goslings' boredom at night, bearing in mind their great need to peck at something!

Natural Feeding for Goslings

Week 1: feed every two hours, i.e. six times a day: Chopped stinging nettles, dandelion, plantain and similar weeds, leftover lettuce and soft vegetables and fruit windfalls, hard-boiled chopped eggs, breadcrumbs in buttermilk (but not too often, because of its binding effect!), rolled oats. Mix these with oystershell. Every other day, add some grated carrot and garlic.

Always provide limestone grit. Sand and small stones are also important; otherwise, the birds will have digestive problems.

Week 2: feed five times a day.

Weeks 3-4: feed four times a day, as above; seed-corn may be added.

Weeks 5-6: feed three times a day. Eliminate hard-boiled eggs. Greens no longer need to be chopped small. Now only 10-20% rolled oats – give seed-corn instead.

Week 7: feed twice a day. No oystershell, but continue limestone

This simple cover, made from a raised board and bricks, protects the goslings' feed from rapacious older birds

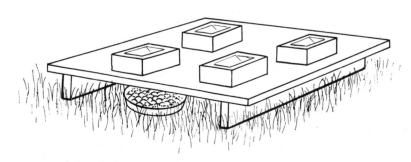

97

grit. No rolled oats, but oats and barley, which may be sprouted. Steamed potatoes or artichokes may be added to the diet. Greens should not only be available from grazing.

Weeks 8-9: feed once a day.

From Week 10: where there is good grazing land, just give a small quantity of oats, or nothing at all.

Older Geese

Geese are very keen on oats, they will eat wheat and barley, but they will not touch rye or maize. The grasses on which geese are to graze should not be too high – it would be best to wait until the first cut has been carried out. Geese should be moved on to different grazing ground before they have given the grass a close crop; otherwise, the only thing that will then grow there will be silverweed (*Potentilla anserina*) which geese will not eat.

Apart from oats, geese love grated carrot, so you could feed them with your own garden produce; a goose will eat 200 or 300 g (7-10½ oz) of this a day. Geese are also very fond of dandelion, young stinging nettles (very nutritious!) and horsetails.

Where there is good grazing land, breeding geese do not require any additional feeding in summer.

Winter Feeding for Breeding Stock

In the morning: steamed potato or artichoke.

At midday: stinging nettles or hay in hanging baskets, greens from kitchen leftovers, dry finely chopped bread (without mould!).

In the evening: barley, oats, possibly sprouted.

Water, limestone grit, sand and granite or flint grit should be given. Once a month, carrot and garlic should be mixed with the potatoes. Stop giving sprouted oats about one month before the start of egg laying. If the breeding goose becomes too fat, cut down on potatoes, corn and bread.

The Run and Grazing Land

If you want to keep geese, it is very important that you have a large area of ground for grazing: a breeding pair with offspring will require between 1500 and 2000 sq m (16,000-21,000 sq ft). Depending on the quality of the grazing, you should reckon on 50-80 birds to the hectare (125-200 birds per acre). In addition to this, if geese are to thrive (and this includes care of feathers), they must have clean water in which they can plunge – up to their chests at least.

Light breeds of geese, especially the younger birds, can fly very high. Consequently, adequate provision needs to be made for fencing them in, to avoid trouble with neighbours. (You may already have had words about your birds: with their strong voices, geese can make quite a racket!)

Because of their highly developed sense of direction, geese often walk more than half a mile to their pasture land. This journey should not, of course, be made across a public roadway without human supervision. In addition, the path to the grazing land should not be stony, if it can be helped, because this can result in injuries to the birds' feet, which will be slow to heal; this will retard the bird's growth rate.

The grazing should not be too overgrown, or else it will be trampled down. Depending on the time of year, therefore, either wait for the first cut, or give it an initial grazing by horses, cows, sheep or goats. Geese need to be moved on at frequent intervals to different grazing land; otherwise, they will eat their way down to the roots of the grass and it will not grow back.

There also need to be trees for shade; alternatively, straw matting can be put up on supports in the grazing area to protect the geese from excessive heat.

Housing

Geese love light and hate damp straw: they will not sleep on it, and soon react with diarrhoea. They are also upset by draughts. Apart from these factors, they have no other requirements for their housing and are impervious to cold.

Simple wooden walls will be sufficient; however, the floor – as we saw with chickens – needs to be firmly based. The walls, floor and windows must be protected against rats, weasels and other hungry predators,

Maximum stocking density for geese is 80 birds per hectare

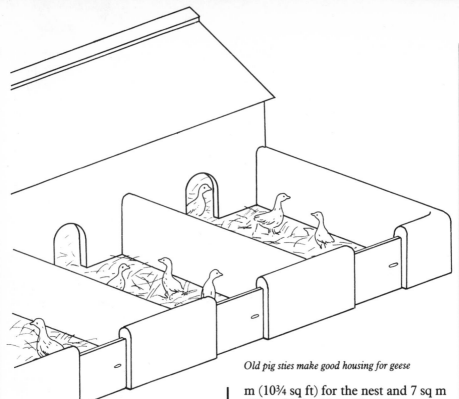

Old pig sties make good housing for geese

by covering them with fine wire netting. The ceiling should be high enough for a person to stand up inside in order to clean out the droppings. When an existing, high-ceilinged building is to be converted for use by geese, a false ceiling should be installed.

Redundant pig sties make very good goose housing; the pens can be divided up so that each breeding pair has one in which their goslings can be hatched and reared. Otherwise, dividing walls of 1 m (3¼ ft) in height can be used. Each goose requires an area of 0.5 sq m (6 sq ft); this means 1 sq m (10¾ sq ft) for the parents, 1 sq m (10¾ sq ft) for the nest and 7 sq m (75 sq ft) for 10 to 15 goslings – i.e. 9 sq m (96 sq ft) for a family pen.

The separate nest boxes (80 × 80 cm/32 × 32 in) should be fixed firmly in place, ideally in a position where they will receive partial light. Since nests are also used as places of refuge outside of the laying season, quarrels will be reduced if each goose has her own nest box.

For ventilation and adequate lighting, it is advisable to have the windows on the south side. These can be opened out in summer, and the opening covered with wire netting.

If the birds enter and leave their quarters through a flap rather than through a door, the flap should be level with the ground, without sharp edges, and fairly large so that a fully grown goose can pass through without difficulty. Geese do not return to their house until late evening, and they may then mistrust this sinister-looking black hole in the wall. If they do, it will be necessary to light their quarters in the evening until all the stragglers are safely inside.

It is not very easy to feed goslings without the adult birds, apparently ravenous, trying to get in on the act. It is, therefore, a good idea, to fit a door to each pen that is only large enough for the goslings to get through. They can then be fed in the front part when bad weather makes it impossible to feed them outside. The doorway to the run should have openings of two different sizes so that, when the weather is good, the goslings can be lured to a separate feeding run, without the adult birds, which can be given a small quantity of greens to keep them quiet.

Only in the autumn, when the young geese are getting fairly large, does it become difficult, and they will then need a normal-sized hatchway; the fully grown, ringed breeding stock must then be kept back from the entrance. A red plastic rake has proved useful in this connection: it seems to have a great effect on all the birds.

It is not a good idea to keep geese alongside other poultry because they will very quickly wet all the straw and eat the other birds' food. The chickens will then spend all day scratching at the straw in the goose house, adding their own droppings to it, as well as taking great interest in the large eggs in the geese's nests when they are out grazing.

Food and water containers should not be fixed inside the housing because these only need to be used there when the snow is so high in winter that the birds are unable to move around outside. It is also advisable to feed the birds outside because this prevents their straw from becoming too soiled. Whenever possible, they should be allowed access to water for bathing, even in winter.

House for three geese and a gander

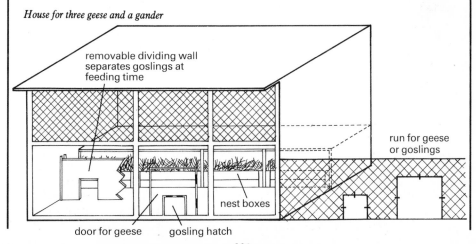

removable dividing wall separates goslings at feeding time

run for geese or goslings

nest boxes

door for geese   gosling hatch

DUCKS

It was not until around 3000 BC that the duck was domesticated. A distinction has to be made between swimming ducks which originate from the mallard, and the domestic Muscovy duck, the flying variety.

The natural habitats of the mallard are Asia, Europe and North America, while the Muscovy duck lived originally in South America. Water is the natural element of the latter, but they are also good flyers. There are a few breeds of domestic duck which have not lost this ability: well known for

Muscovy ducks are good fliers as well as swimmers

this retained instinct are the dwarf ducks and high-nesting ducks (including the domestic Muscovy).

Ducks do not see as well at a distance as geese, and their sense of hearing is also poorer. Nor does their sense of taste match that of the goose. The sense of smell, on the other hand, is well developed, in comparison with other birds.

Bills and Eating

Their broad, long bills are well suited to wet, soft food, but they tend to have problems with eating finely ground corn if it has not been moistened. The duck has a more developed filtering bill than the goose, and uses it to obtain food from the water or from very wet mud. It squeezes the water out through the serrations at the sides of its bill, retaining the edible solids in its mouth.

Greens are accepted indiscriminately; the tender leaf content must not, however, be very high. They are much more sensitive to the temperature of their drinking water than other birds, and are certainly happier drinking it at 15°C (59°F) than, say, at 25°C (77°F).

They will eat any amount of snails and green caterpillars and other insects, which are of absolutely no interest to chickens, along with any other small life forms they happen to come across. Cases have been reported of carp doing particularly well when ducks have taken up residence on their pools. However, if there are small fish in the pond, care must be taken: the ducks would soon swallow them up.

Courtship, Breeding and General Behaviour

Ducks live in loose groupings without any particular order of precedence. Only during the breeding season in spring are any paired relationships in wild ducks to be observed, and these dissolve before brooding is complete.

Courting and pairing are still quite pronounced in the case of the wild mallard. In the autumn, the drakes come together for 'mock courtship', during which they engage in preliminary mock mating with one another, producing a grunting, whistling sound which seems to result from the compression of air in the windpipe. Drakes amuse themselves in this way until the ducks come in the spring.

At this time, fierce battles take place among the drakes, and these are pursued relentlessly. The females select their drakes by chasing after them and swimming behind them, acting in a threatening way to any other drakes. If the chosen drake joins in with the threats against another drake, this is a sign that pairing has been established. If, on the other hand, the chosen drake fails to respond, the duck will look for another male and behave threateningly towards her first choice.

If the duck and the drake are in agreement, they dip their heads faster and faster into the water. Finally, the duck invites copulation by lowering her body in the water. The Muscovy drake frisks for a while around the

Ducklings hatch after 28 days and swim when a few days old. Muscovies need 35 days

duck, and then mounts her – this happens suddenly and briefly. He may repeat this process – even with other ducks.

In the case of the domestic duck, however, the courting ritual is no longer observed. The female indicates to one or more drakes, by gestures with her neck and body, that she is ready to be covered. Alternatively, the drakes, without any warning, mount any one of the female birds.

Brooding and Hatching

For the brief period of their partnership with the drakes, ducks living in the wild take the lead in flying, in mating and in the search for a nesting place. The duck builds the nest in two to three days, lines it with down and then lays up to 18 eggs. She has a longer laying period than the chicken – up to 14 consecutive days. Fertilization can continue for up to five days following mating. One- or two-year-old drakes are most reliable in this respect.

During its building and up to the start of brooding, the drake protects the nest. He then loses his colourful wedding coat through moulting and, wearing his plain clothes, abandons the brooding duck.

The ducklings communicate with one another while still in their eggs. This communication can also accelerate hatching when more developed eggs (i.e. eggs that were hatched and incubated before others) are present in the nest; these last laid eggs are then able to hatch with up to 11 hours less development time.

The wild duck will usually brood for between 24 and 28 days, with most ducklings hatching in April. An exception to this is the Muscovy duck, for whom incubation lasts 35 days and the duck broods two or three times a year. Domestic ducks have almost lost the brooding instinct. The most reliable brooders are the domestic Muscovy ducks who, like their wild cousins, may even sit on the nest twice or three times a year.

When the ducklings are ready to hatch, they establish contact with their mother by means of their cheeping sounds, and the mother responds more and more loudly as hatching progresses. After hatching, the ducklings greet their mother and her sisters with cheeping sounds. They communicate their need for help by means of the distress cry to which only their own mother responds.

The ducklings that hatch during the first four hours are mostly all females. Following this, there is a period in which both males and females are born; and then, during the last four hours, the ducklings that hatch are almost all males.

Just one day after hatching, the mother leads the ducklings to water for a swim. She stays with them for around two months, until they are able to fly. When they have truly left the nest, the duck loses all her feathers. (Pekin ducks, however, moult every eight to ten weeks.)

Later Life

There is no obvious pecking order among ducklings. Ten days after hatching, they have a good warm downy coat and no longer need to stick together for warmth, preferring to keep to themselves. With adult ducks, this preference for keeping at a distance can be clearly seen when the birds sleep and eat. This means that there is no need to establish a clear order of precedence since the ducks prefer to keep out of one another's way. Nevertheless, nervous or easily frightened ducks need the togetherness found in a group so that they will feel protected and have the courage to make long excursions and reconnaissance trips. (As with geese, the duck's sense of direction is very good.)

Ducks grow their pinions and tail feathers in three to four weeks – i.e. about two weeks earlier than geese do. By Day 130 the duck's body is fully grown; thereafter only the heart and brain grow until Day 140. After some seven months, ducks are sexually mature.

In the case of the mallard, the sexes are easily distinguishable by the striking colouring of the male bird's feathers. At 12 weeks, Muscovy ducks are only half the weight of the drakes; indeed, the weight difference is even more pronounced later on. Even with domestic breeds, in which the feathers of both sexes are identical, the drake and the duck can readily be distinguished by their voices: the duck quacks loudly and clearly, whereas the male emits a hoarse, soft, deep croak.

Ducks are typically waterfowl who

need water to clean their feathers if they are to feel happy. They engage in the same comfort behaviour as geese.

Breeds and Buying

Today, there are some 105 different breeds of duck, which can be divided into four main groups:

1 Laying ducks which produce up to 250 eggs a year.
2 Dual-purpose breeds which are good both for eggs and for meat.
3 Ducks bred for their meat, weighing up to 5 kg (11 lb).
4 Dwarf and ornamental ducks.

Laying Ducks

Unfortunately, it has become very difficult to sell duck eggs, even though only a few years ago they were regarded as a welcome delicacy. Since then, however, it has become known that they can contain typhoid and paratyphoid bacilli. This is due primarily to the fact that ducks will lay their eggs anywhere, even in the most dirty conditions. For this reason, laying ducks should be kept in their house until around 10 o'clock in the morning so that they will lay their eggs in the clean straw.

Laying ducks, like productive laying hens, do not carry a great deal of meat and therefore belong to the light breeds. The best known are probably the hardy **Indian Runner** and the **Khaki Campbell**, which lay around 200 eggs, each weighing about 75 g (2½ oz), between autumn and spring. These ducks require a large run, but are quite happy with a low fence and a small water bowl.

A typical feature of the Indian Runner is its almost upright gait; this can result in problems with its legs and feet which are very slender. The drake weighs around 2 kg (4½ lb); the duck is somewhat lighter and will occasionally brood. There are eight different known colourings.

Dual-purpose Breeds

Among these is the equally hardy **Pomeranian** duck, which weighs up to 3 kg (6½ lb) and lays 100-120 eggs of between 70 and 80 g (2¼-2½ oz) from February to June. This duck needs to have somewhere to swim, and be surrounded by a low fence. It can be black or blue in colour.

The **Orpington** duck, weighing 3.5 kg (8 lb) or more, lays up to 180 eggs of 70 g (2¼ oz) each. For fertilization to take place, these ducks need a brook or pool to swim in, but they are happy with a small run. Moreover, their food requirements are very small. They can be easily recognized by their yellowish-brown feathers, but they can also be blue in colour.

Ducks Bred for their Meat

Typical meat birds are the **French Rouen** ducks. These weigh up to 4 kg (8¾ lb) and lay between 70 and 90 eggs at 80 g (2½ oz). In appearance, they are very similar to mallards, and the drake also grows the so-called 'wedding clothes' breeding plumage. These ducks need only a small run, but they must have access to water if fertilization is to take place. Unfortunately, Rouen ducks make very unreliable broodies.

The equally robust **Aylesbury** duck, one of the more popular British breeds, weighs up to 3.5 kg (8 lb), or more in the case of older birds. She lays up to 100 eggs at 80 g (2½ oz) and must have access to water for swimming. These ducks' feathers are pure white.

The **Pekin** duck comes in two different varieties. The **American Pekin** duck has a horizontal body posture, white feathers and weighs up to 3 kg (6½ lb). The **German Pekin** duck has a more upright posture and bright yellow feathers, and weighs up to 3.5 kg (8 lb). This duck lays around 100 eggs at 75 g (2½ oz), but rarely broods. Their voices are something of a problem: they are very loud and they are used constantly. In addition, they are fairly shy birds. The run needs to be as large as possible because they like to go off wandering. They also need access to water.

The **Muscovy** duck is closer to the goose family than to the duck family, both in terms of its origin and in its behaviour. This is the only remaining domestic breed that is reliable for brooding purposes, and it engages in this activity two to three times a year. It can lay between 40 and 100 70-g (2¼ oz) eggs a year, but since it is a reliable brooder, there are rarely more than 40 or 50 eggs (brooding lasts 35 days).

The Muscovy is also rightly known as a flying duck. This breed needs an unlimited run or it will need to have one of its wings clipped – i.e. cutting the pinions on one of its wings. A painless procedure, this prevents the ducks from flying because they are no longer able to keep their balance.

The Muscovy drake weighs up to 5 kg (11 lb), and the duck around 2.5 kg (5½ lb). Their meat is very succulent, low in fat and somewhat darker than that of other ducks. Another feature of this breed is that they have very quiet voices. Seven different colourings are known.

Ornamental Ducks

Among ornamentals are the **high-nesting flying ducks**. The female of this type nests on trees 2-3 m (6½-10 ft) high, and entices the ducklings down to the ground – they drop without hesitation. The offspring are reared by the parents together. Since they also mate with wild mallards, a considerable amount of cross-breeding has occurred. To prevent this from taking place, therefore, it is necessary to keep them in an enclosure.

Brooding and Rearing

Domestic ducks tend to lay their eggs between January and March, and they start to brood some two weeks after the first eggs are laid. Since most breeds are very unreliable for breeding, it is worth considering whether the duck should be placed in separate quarters (as recommended earlier for broody hens) for this period – two weeks for laying and 24 to 28 days for brooding.

In the wild state, all drakes abandon their mates early in the season and may even migrate to separate summer habitats. Domestic drakes, however, show more of an inclination to remain faithful to their mates.

During the laying period, the duck should be put together with the drake every four to five days so that the eggs can be fertilized; alternatively, the drake may remain with her throughout, provided that they get on with one another.

Brooding Quarters

Divide up your duck-house into separate compartments. Provide each with its own fenced-off portion of land for a run (which still needs to have good ground cover) and with a clean water bowl. The run should not be too large otherwise it will entice the duck away from brooding. Since ducks are group orientated, it should also be divided with fences so that the birds can always keep in touch with one another.

As with the goose, the nest box should be lined with a turf measuring about 60 × 60 cm (24 × 24 in). Ducks will favour a nest box that is covered by bundles of straw or reeds tied together at the top to form a cone or 'nest hut'.

Flying ducks which brood faithfully two or three times a year are little trouble, but they must be allowed to get used to their nest box. During the first days of laying, it is best if they are kept in their quarters until 10 o'clock in the morning to prevent them from laying their eggs elsewhere.

As in the case of geese, the first egg should be left in the nest and marked for identification purposes. A few china eggs to replace the eggs removed for hatching will persuade the duck to remain with the same nest. The selection and storage of the eggs should be carried out as described for chickens.

Early Life

After 24 to 28 days (or 35 days in the case of flying ducks) the ducklings will hatch; the duck will now take care of them herself without difficulty. Ducks which do not have a mother should be reared in the same

Nest for ducks made with upturned turf and straw roof

way as goslings. In the case of ducklings, however, the temperature can be reduced to 24°C (75.2°F) on Day 10.

Ducklings should have a continuous supply of dry straw. However, this must not be too finely shredded or the ducklings will eat it. This may stick in the crop in their throats, leading to fatal consequences.

Since ducklings are very fond of splashing, it is a good idea to separate the feeding place from their housing. If possible, pour some sand around the drinker so that any splashes will be absorbed. It will, of course, be necessary to replace the sand at frequent intervals. Gratings are another possibility for keeping the feeding place dry, although these can sometimes cause injuries to the birds' feet; they have to be frequently brushed free of droppings.

It is also important for ducks to be able to dip their heads past the eyes into water, yet not be able to stand in the water. In any event, a stone or an upturned flowerpot should be used to prevent the ducks from bathing in the water or from splashing it over the edge.

In any water container into which a duck might enter, there needs to be some means of ensuring that the water level does not drop too much thereby preventing the ducklings from getting out; many ducklings have drowned because of this. It is also important to place water containers far away from the feeding place since ducks are in the habit of stuffing their bills full of food and then plunging them into a nearby source of water to 'gargle' through it.

Later Life

There should never be more than 20 ducks in one group; otherwise, the birds will become nervous. Once the young birds have grown their feathers, they can be put with the older ducks. Birds chosen as breeding stock should be put together in the autumn because it takes ducks a long time to get used to one another.

After 9 to 12 weeks, the ducks will be ready for killing. Older birds will have more fat, but this is not popular with consumers.

Feeding Ducks

Ducks love soft food. Since they are omnivorous, they can be fed with kitchen scraps. Their favourite cereal is maize, if possible soaked until it is slightly swollen; they are also happy to eat wheat and barley, whereas oats should only be given to young ducks in the form of rolled oat feed, or ground and mixed with other food. They also like seed oats, but are not at all happy with rye.

Chickweed and other plants are readily eaten, preferably mixed with greens. Among their favourite greens are also common duckweed (*Lemna minor*) and similar weeds. These grow from June to July at the shallow end of standing water. The small, green, lens-shaped fronds float on the surface, trailing tiny roots beneath them in the water. In the past, this plant was gathered and fed to ducklings as an important part of their diets.

Ducks – and ducklings, too – must have access to grit and sand which,

A typical house for a small flock of ducks

once swallowed, help to break down their food in the stomach. If they cannot get this, it will lead to serious intestinal problems.

Ducks require a high protein intake. If they do not get enough, they grow fat. Buttermilk or curds can be given to them to meet this need. Fish meal is rich in protein, although it does tend to affect the flavour of the meat. This also applies if ducks are given too much fresh fish, and fish meal contains traces of perchlorethylene.

Stinging nettles (older leaves will have to be chopped up) are also high in protein, as are all the insects which are eaten throughout the day. If you have a garden with a large population of ants or snails, you can allow ducks, under supervision, to harvest them for you. Ant larvae and earthworms are rich in protein and are eaten with relish.

Feeding Ducklings

Ducklings like soft food but always want to dip their full bills into water to 'gargle' through it; they then wipe their caked bills on their feathers. The other young birds then peck at this 'appetizing' down until bare patches of skin are visible. For this reason – at least for the first few days when the ducklings are still sensitive to the cold – no soft food should be given them if at all possible. They will be happy to eat rolled oats.

Week 1: feed five to six times a day, putting down as much as can be eaten in 15 minutes.

Rolled oats mixed with a little ground limestone and yeast, seed-corn, breadcrumbs, finely chopped leftover lettuce, finely chopped nettles and other greens, hard-boiled finely chopped eggs, buttermilk, whey, grit, oystershell or sterilized, crushed egg shell.

Week 2: four to five times a day. Omit eggs; add fruit and vegetable leftovers.

Week 3: feed three times a day. Omit limestone; give moist, crumbled ground mash made from maize, wheat, barley, wheat-bran, perhaps mixed with whey or buttermilk; also steamed potatoes or artichokes. The birds will look for greens themselves; when there is not enough in the run, a basket of them can be hung up in the run.

From Week 4: feed as for adult birds. Soaked maize, moistened grain mix, seed-corn, windfalls, vegetable leftovers, kitchen waste (including meat and fish, but be sure there are no bones), bone-meal prepared by a butcher, steamed potatoes or artichokes, soaked bread, a large quantity of greens, grit, oystershell or sterilized, crushed egg shell.

Housing and Runs

As with geese, housing ducks requires little expenditure, but it must be well planned to avoid unnecessary work and problems.

A few questions should be cleared up at the outset:

- Is there sufficient water to hand? Are there fish in the water?
- How large an area for the run is available? A pair of ducks need 400 sq m (4300 sq ft).
- Will the land be fenced in? If so, how high?
- Are there any local government restrictions on garden poultry-keeping?
- What are the neighbours' feelings?
- Is there an existing building that can be converted, or will it be necessary to obtain planning permission for a new one?
- How large is the housing to be? Each duck must have 0.5 sq m (5½ sq in) of housing space.
- What will be done with the eggs? Can they be consumed in your own household or do you have buyers for them?

Windows and Doors

Ducks are easily frightened so windows should be as high as possible to prevent their being startled by people passing by. If necessary, a window facing on to a street should be boarded over to keep out noise and light. Fine wire mesh can be hung over openings in the summer to replace the windows. Provision

However they are housed, ducks must be able to get their heads under water

be careful when entering their quarters. If more than four or five ducks are being kept, it is advisable to incorporate a walk-way into the building: this will act as a sort of bridge across the straw (*see* diagram). This will divide the area into four, and the ducks will be able to walk beneath it.

If a straw nest hut is set up in each quarter, each housing one drake plus three to four ducks, every 'family' will have its own section, the eggs will in all probability be laid within the nest huts, and even the drake will have a place of refuge. This means the building will house 20 ducks – a reasonable size – and the division will provide a greater sense of tranquillity. At the narrow end of the housing, straw matting can also be used to create separate bays for the brooding ducks, each having her own run.

If, on the other hand, you are only keeping one drake and three ducks, it will be enough to have 4 sq m (43 sq ft) of housing space. A straw nest hut is built in each quarter, and at brooding time, these can be separated from one another by low wire mesh walls.

If the walls are only about 1 m (3¼ ft) high, it should be possible to open up either the roof or the front to clean out the birds' droppings or remove the eggs. Small air slits above the doorway to the run – 20-30 cm (8-12 in) in length and covered with wire mesh – will allow sufficient air and light to enter. If the walls are about 2 m (6½ ft) high, there should be a narrow stretch of window along one of the longer walls, with wire netting over the opening so that the windows can be opened out in good weather.

should be made in large duck houses for good ventilation without draughts.

The pop-hole for ducklings should be at ground level, and must be suited to the size of the breed for which they are intended – about 30 to 40 sq cm (4.65-6.2 sq in). A door or pop-hole both at the front and at the back makes it possible to let the ducks out into the south-facing runs during the breeding period and, for the rest of the year, into the large communal run.

Housing

Ducks lay their eggs in straw and then cover them over; you must therefore

There should be a firm base to the housing so that the ducks' quarters can be kept clean and dry. This should also be covered with fine wire netting to keep rats out, as for geese and hens.

Run and Pond

Provision should be made for shady places in the run – i.e. under trees, bushes or straw matting supported on poles. If there is a pond or stream, the bank should be stabilized using some form of netting covered with gravel; otherwise, it will soon collapse and become a mudbath.

If a pond is to be dug, it should be lined with a 30-cm (12 in) thick layer of clay. Moulded plastic will not stand up for long to the claws at the ends of the webbed feet of ducks and geese. A flat bank or edge will also need to be stabilized in the same way.

Another possibility is a large, flat, ready-cast concrete pool with gravel spread all around the edges. It is a good idea here to bore a hole at the lowest point to link up with a drainage pipe. It will then be possible to let out

A simple, moveable, home-made house for ducks

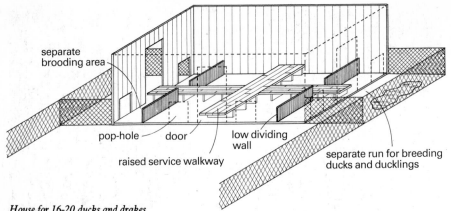

separate brooding area

pop-hole   door   low dividing wall

raised service walkway

separate run for breeding ducks and ducklings

House for 16-20 ducks and drakes

polluted water and refill the pool with fresh. The entrance to the drainage pipe should be so designed that the ducks are not able to tamper with it; ideally, it should be covered by a heavy stone.

In any event, the birds should always be able to leave the water at will, even when the level is low. For this reason, a sunken bath tub is not a good idea. An old, flat shower base, on the other hand, may be a possibility. However, you will still need to watch out for the ducklings because, to begin with, they will not be big enough to get out again if the water level is too low. A number of flattened stones at the edge of the water can be a help in this connection.

If the ducks have an unlimited run with, alongside it, somewhere to swim, you will need to drive the birds home in the evening or they will spend the night there. Since they would soon be discovered by foxes and weasels, it is necessary to keep them locked up overnight. If the ducks are fed at a fixed time each evening, they will quickly get used to

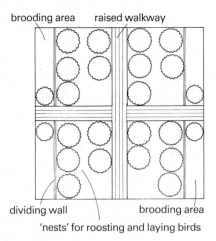

brooding area   raised walkway

dividing wall   brooding area

'nests' for roosting and laying birds

Plan view

this and make their way home of their own free will.

When cleaning out their houses, or when carrying out any other work in the immediate vicinity, it is essential that vigorous movements, loud noises and banging be avoided. Otherwise, these nervous birds will always panic as soon as they see people.

Smallholding with a pond suitable for ducks

114

TURKEYS

The turkey originates from North, Central and South America, and was domesticated in Mexico in about 2500 BC. During the intervening period, the weight of the bird has been increased through breeding from 10 kg (22 lb) to 18 kg (30 lb).

Like the chicken, the wild turkey is a ground-scratching bird; it is also land-based, able to run very fast and with great persistence. Even today, the domesticated turkey enjoys running over large areas of grazing land, but it no longer scratches the ground in search for food. At night and when they want to rest during the day, turkeys like to fly and perch in a tree; they prefer branches which overhang water since these offer greater protection from predators.

Turkeys see well at a distance, but their near vision is not so good. If food has been scattered over the ground, they will only find it by chance.

General and Courtship Behaviour

The males and females live in separate flocks on the basis of their sex. Young females in the wild spend the winter months with the older hens, going round in large flocks. The males also join forces and live together until the mating season, when contact with the female flock is re-established.

The two groups have different behavioural patterns. Whereas the male – known as the *stag* or the *tom* – is unconcerned about any order of precedence with respect to the other males, the females – or *hens* – insist on establishing a pecking order, just as female chickens do. However, they peck at one another to a greater extent than chickens. The males and females do not fight among themselves, even as *poults* (chicks).

Fighting and Panic

The stags and the hens use the same fighting tactics. They extend the skin flaps on their heads and spread their wings; then the stag flattens out his tail feathers, while the hen raises her tail. Finally, they stand – stag against stag, or hen against hen – and threaten one another with piercing, high-pitched sounds; old hens produce deeper, grumbling sounds. They circle one another until one of them suddenly jumps up, clawing the other with its feet. The fight now becomes more intense, the two opponents pecking one another on the neck or grasping hold of the other bird's skin flaps and tugging at them.

When one of the two combatants wishes to give in, it draws in its skin flaps, lowers its wings and tries to run away, with the winner in pursuit, still pecking at it. Female turkeys are very strong fighters; if there is no escape, the fight will often end in the death of the bird which has tried to escape.

Wild turkey hen

Since turkeys have very fixed behavioural patterns and are very poor at adapting to new situations, their only reaction to a frightening or tense situation is to run away in a panic. When they are kept in enclosed runs, they will react so extremely to situations they perceive as frightening that they will crush one another to death in a corner of the fence. Once their instinctive behaviour has been triggered – i.e. they have an inborn

reaction to an external stimulus – they will follow it through to the end, whatever the cost.

These birds do not have the ability to 're-program' their behaviour. A typical example is the way a brooding turkey will behave. When she is sitting on the nest brooding, she can think of nothing else, so she will continue to sit there until she starves. It is therefore necessary to remove her bodily from the nest each day – to which she will react strongly – so that she will have an opportunity to eat, drink and defecate, and the eggs will be able to cool.

Courtship and Mating

The courting behaviour of both wild and domestic turkeys has remained the same. The stag unfurls his feathers into a circular shape, in the same way that a peacock does, and glides his feathers a little above ground level, continually lowering his head; his skin flaps swell and redden and he struts around solemnly with a gobbling, snorting sound.

If the hen is willing to mate, she will stoop down in front of him while the stag continues to strut around her for a short while. He then mounts her, standing on her hips, with alternate feet, until he is low enough for their cloacae to come into contact. No follow-up behaviour takes place.

However, turkeys sometimes have problems with direction, and a stag may mount the female bird the wrong way round, often causing irreparable damage due to his great weight. In addition, stags very soon become exhausted because the courting ceremony requires a lot of effort. They also produce an excessive amount of heat, so to ensure good fertilization in summer, it is important that there are cool, shady places available to these birds.

Following mating, some of the females will mount other hens, acting like stags. Hens lower down in the pecking order will often submit to pairing of this kind, as we saw earlier in the case of chickens.

Breeding Behaviour

After copulation, which will fertilize around 12 eggs, the hens will not be ready to mate again for five days. (Nevertheless, sometimes the sperm in the oviduct can still fertilize eggs after seven weeks.) Two days after mating, the eggs will be fertilized. A laying session can last for 13 to 50 days. Turkeys which have already brooded a number of times before will lay more fertilized and hatchable eggs.

One particularly unusual feature of turkeys is that hens which have been kept strictly separate from stags are sometimes able to lay eggs from which poults (baby turkeys) will hatch. This is known as *parthenogenesis*, from the Greek words meaning 'virgin production'.

In 1958, in a well-documented case, a healthy male poult (chick), hatched from an unfertilized turkey egg, went on to father a number of healthy turkeys. Since then, strains have been developed in which 40 per cent of the eggs will undergo parthenogenetic development. An interesting aspect of this is that only male birds are produced in this way.

Brooding and Hatching

Wild turkey hens brood at the end of February in scratched-out hollows in the ground, protected by shrubs and bushes; they then line the nest with leaves and feathers. On Day 27, the unhatched poults establish contact with the mother by cheeping; they then remain silent until they have hatched the next day. This cheeping prevents the hen from pecking them to death.

After 48 hours, the poults go on their first excursion with their mother, who very soon extends the length of these outings. Like goslings, poults are very impressionable during the first 72 hours.

Vocalization

The turkey hen calls her offspring with a low-pitched, beckoning sound. The poults make a complaining sound when they lose their way, emit cries of pain when they are pecked, and make vocal contact sounds between themselves and a gentle twittering sound when they are about to go to sleep.

Grown turkeys make a warbling sound when presented with their favourite food. In the face of danger, they emit an alarm cry, but it is not until a few weeks after hatching that young poults react to this. There are different alarm cries – e.g. enemies on the ground, enemies in the air, enemies in the vicinity – and turkeys react differently to each one.

Early Life

At 14 days, the poults are already perching on low branches of trees, and at eight weeks, the young birds are fully feathered. The poults do not really recognize one another very clearly until the first playful squabbles over rank in the order of precedence at three months. These fights intensify noticeably, reaching their height when the young birds are five months old.

Adult Birds

Domestic turkeys become sexually mature between Days 200 and 250, while, in wild turkeys this does not take place until they are two years old. Domesticated turkeys live for about 15 years.

Just like chickens, turkeys like to take dust-baths. They preen their feathers by gripping the shafts with their beaks and pulling these through their beaks. If the feathers are soiled or frayed, turkeys tend to eat their own feathers.

It is not advisable to keep turkeys alongside other types of poultry. While it is true that turkeys like to live in large groups and do not seem to mind which birds comprise these, they *are* rather quarrelsome birds and, because of their large size, are quite happy to take on even a cock, who will be lucky to escape with his life. There are also feeding problems because the turkeys will keep the other birds away from the trough. Moreover, chickens can transfer the germs causing the disease blackhead to turkeys, without being affected by it themselves.

Breeds and Buying

Despite many years of breeding, the turkey has mainly changed in terms of body weight and colouring, so we do not speak so much of different breeds as of different strains. There are light, medium and heavy strains.

Among the light strains – in which hens weigh 4 to 5 kg (8¾-11 lb), and stags 6 to 9 kg (13-20 lb) – are the

Courtship behaviour of both wild and domestic turkeys is similar

Crollwitzer and the small **Beltsville**, as well as yellow, red, blue and copper-coloured types.

Among the medium-weight birds – hens 5 to 7 kg (11-15½ lb), and stags 8 to 12 kg (17¾-26½ lb) – are the red **Bourbon**, **Red Wing** and **Black** turkey.

Among the heavy strains – hens 6 to 8 kg (13½-17¾ lb), and stags 9 to 15 kg (20-33 lb) – are the **Bronze**, the **Black Wing** and the **White** turkey. The **Broad-breasted Bronze** is particularly heavy – the hens can weigh between 7 and 9 kg (15½-20 lb) and the stags up to 18 kg (40 lb).

The very heaviest turkeys are **Broad-breasted Whites**, which hold the world weight record for a turkey – 37.6 kg (82 lb 14 oz), set in London in December 1987.

Since aggressive behaviour is hereditary, the individual strains also come with varying temperaments. The small Beltsville is the most peaceable, next comes the Broad-breasted White, followed by the Bronze; the most aggressive of all are the Black turkeys.

The number of eggs laid by turkeys in a year varies between 60 and 180, weighing 70 to 80 g (2¼-2½ oz) each. Output is dependent on the age of the bird: one-year-old turkeys are the most prolific.

The two sexes can be distinguished by looking at their heads: the stags have no markings, while the hens have very scant head covering. After 12 to 14 weeks the skin flaps can be pulled over the beak in the stag; this is not possible with the female.

Brooding and Rearing

The flock of a turkey stag can consist of 8 up to a maximum of 15 hens, depending on the weight of the strain in question. Older toms should have fewer hens in their flock.

Brooding

As a rule, turkey hens are broody between February and May, depending on when they were hatched. They should be around eight months old at brooding time. The best time is at the end of March or the beginning of April; this means that the poults will hatch at the end of April or the beginning of May. Brooding lasts for 28 days.

Turkey hens can also be made to

brood by sitting them on nests containing warmed china eggs, placing a large basket over them and letting them out once a day; after a maximum of three days, the hens will begin to cluck. However, I feel that this is a questionable practice since, in most cases, turkeys will brood of their own free will without having to be compelled in this way.

Conditions for brooding, the nest (80 × 80 cm/32 × 32 in) and the selection of eggs (up to 18) for hatching are the same as already described for chickens.

It is essential that the hen not be able to reach food when sitting on the nest; otherwise, she will defecate on the eggs. In any case, the eggs need to cool periodically. Without food, the hen may still be disinclined to leave the nest – even though she is starving.

It will therefore be necessary to lift her carefully once a day. It sometimes happens that she will continue to 'brood' where she is put down on the ground, taking no notice of food placed under her nose. This problem can be helped by enlisting the help of the bird's jealous instinct: allow a couple of other birds to enter the brooding quarters; as soon as they make a bid for the food, the hen will suddenly come back to her senses, fend off the other birds and eat.

After Hatching

It is essential that the young poults be fed the first day after they hatch; otherwise, their growth rate will be adversely affected and this will only come to light when they are four to six weeks old. The food must be rich in protein – around 30 per cent of the total. Poults should therefore be given a lot of milk and hard-boiled eggs (*see also* the instructions for feeding chicks).

It must be remembered that the poults have poor eyesight, and food must be put right under their beaks. The same is true for the heating lamp. Poults are often unable to find their way back to the source of warmth. It therefore makes more sense to have them reared by a broody who will let them bury themselves in her feathers.

There can, however, be a great confusion when two broody turkeys rear poults alongside one another. Since the mother birds do not notice which poults are pushing their way under their wings, one hen may end up looking after five or six young while the other is caring for 25 or more. Of course, this number cannot all fit under her wings, so some of the poults will freeze, sometimes to death. It is therefore essential that turkey hens be separated when rearing their young.

Disease Prevention

It is also important that the straw on the floor of the housing – around 15-20 cm (6-8 in) deep – be kept dry at all times for the poults are very sensitive to damp. Sun and fresh air are indispensable. Damp straw, too little warmth and/or stale air will soon lead to blackhead disease (*see* next chapter).

To be on the safe side, a preventive medicine can be obtained from the vet and mixed with the birds' food for the first three weeks, since losses caused by this disease can be very high during this period. For this reason, a run that has been used by chickens (who can pass on the disease) should not be used for other poultry for one year, if possible.

The poults need to be protected from rain and cold weather for the first eight weeks of their life, until the feathers have grown over their backs. After that point, the birds will be comparatively hardy.

Growth

The heavy strains of turkey put on around 65 g (just over 2 oz) a day up to the age of 12 weeks. After that, the protein content of the food is not so significant; instead, the calorie content becomes more important. From the outset, the females are lighter than the males. At 20 weeks, medium-weight birds are ready for slaughter; heavy strains are not ready for another five weeks.

Feeding

Turkeys are fed in the same way as chickens. An abundant supply of greens found in a good-sized run is supplemented by soft food or mash in the mornings and around 75 g (2½ oz) of corn in the evenings. Grit and sand should be freely available.

Housing and Runs

Housing for turkeys can be arranged as for chickens, although the perches need to be stouter (10 cm/4 in thick) and placed further apart as well as further out from the back wall, although they can be at the same height. A good rule is 80 cm (32 in) from the ground and 80 cm (32 in) between adjacent perches. The last perch should be at least 50 cm (20 in) away from the back wall.

A turkey needs around 40 to 50 cm (16-20 in) of space on a perch. Thought must also be given to perches for the young birds (again, at the same height). Up to the age of eight weeks, they should stay with the mother bird overnight in a separate rearing enclosure.

The nest boxes must be on level ground, positioned in half light. They should measure 60 × 60 cm (24 × 24 in) and be constructed in the same way as those for chickens. It is best if the nest boxes are placed a small distance apart, on top of a layer of linoleum on which the straw can be spread, one nest to each bird.

If this is not done, the female birds will display the unusual behaviour of squeezing into an already occupied nest. They will even roll eggs from their neighbour's nest into their own or pull the straw out of it. The linoleum, or perhaps a thick layer of pine needles, will then prevent the eggs from being crushed. It is therefore advisable to carry out a check each morning to ensure that everything is as it should be, especially since turkeys often tend to continue sitting on the eggs, rather than getting up once a day.

In very bad weather in the winter, the turkeys should be kept in their quarters and fed there. For this reason, their housing needs to be of sufficient size, with 1 sq m (10¾ sq ft) of floor space per bird.

Turkeys need to have draught-free housing

The walls do not need any special insulation, as is the case with chickens, since turkeys are unaffected by cold. However, it should be impossible for the wind to blow through cracks, although good ventilation, without draughts, is very important. Windows should be as large as possible and can, in summer, be replaced by wire netting. The doorway to the run should measure approximately 60 × 60 cm (24 × 24 in).

The floor must, of course, be covered with a good layer (to a depth of about 10 cm/4 in) of dry straw.

The Run

This should be fenced in to a height of at least 2 m (6½ ft). Low bushes around the edges are very useful for shielding the birds from the cold ground winds to which they are very sensitive. Large bushes and trees are also important for providing shade and somewhere to perch.

Trees should be some distance from the fence; otherwise, it will be easy for the turkeys to escape. For young birds, it is a good idea if there are large branches with offshoots reaching down to the ground, so that the birds can easily climb up on to the branch.

Since turkeys are quite happy to lay their eggs in the open, one or two nests can be set up under bushes, which will provide protection from bad weather. This will prevent the birds from laying their eggs where they may be mislaid or soiled.

The feeding and watering places in the run should always be kept in fixed positions because turkeys find it very hard to adapt to changes. The covered sand-box in which the birds can take a dust-bath must be placed in a shady spot, as with chickens.

You should provide at least 350 sq m (3750 sq ft) of run for each breeding pair if you expect to rear around 10 poults. Each bird needs an area of 30 to 50 sq m (320-530 sq ft).

POULTRY DISEASES

Many poultry diseases are caused by incorrect stock management – e.g. restricted movement, insufficient fresh air, draughts, excessively dry or humid air, wrong feeding. However, if you keep your birds properly, you will seldom run into problems with their health.

Unfortunately, too much onus is often put on the vet when poultry diseases occur. When in doubt, a sick bird should be killed to release it from its distress. The carcass should then be sent to a veterinary laboratory to ascertain the exact cause of the illness. This is important since there are diseases which can spread as epidemics and which must therefore be countered very quickly. Sick birds that are not killed but treated should be kept separate from the others.

Twice a year, the birds' housing should be thoroughly cleaned. After you have 'mucked out' the housing (which should be done once a week), the perches, manure board and nests should be scrubbed with soap and water and left in the sun to dry. Floors should be hosed with water and scrubbed, and once a year the walls should be whitewashed.

Sand for the dust-bath should be replaced when it is dirty. The addition of wood ash will prevent infestation by vermin.

If a strongly alkaline soft soap is used (pH value 11-12), it will not usually be necessary to use any other form of disinfectant. It may be helpful to use a blow-lamp in inaccessible corners. Many diseases are related to the pH value of the air. Litmus paper, which can be obtained from a chemist, will change to a yellowish-green colour if the atmosphere is somewhat acid (pH value of 6.5). The ammonia vapour which is given off by wet droppings is responsible for alkaline air in the birds' housing, and this can lead to disease. In this case, litmus paper turns blue.

Fruit vinegar in soft food or a vinegar/water solution that has evaporated into the air can have a positive influence on the health of the birds' respiratory systems, provided that a thorough mucking out has taken place. Finely chopped garlic in constantly fresh water and regular cleaning of the birds' quarters can be effective in preventing worms or combating them. In the summer a good supply of greens, from as wide a variety of plants as possible, should be given to make up for any vitamin deficiency; in winter, seed-corn can be given for the same purpose.

A-Z of Ailments

Aspergillosis

Symptoms: rattling breathing, diarrhoea, exhaustion to the point of death. Primarily in young birds. After slaughter: small lumps and mould in the intestines.
Cause: mould fungus in the food and straw; not contagious.

Bacillary White Diarrhoea

See Diarrhoea and Related Diseases

Blackhead

See Diarrhoea and Related Diseases

Broken Legs and Wings

Symptoms: the part of the body in question hangs limp, cannot be moved or used for support.
Treatment: put on a splint and keep separate for two or three weeks. In the case of serious injuries, it is better to have the bird put down.

Bronchitis

See Colds

Bunions

Symptoms: the surfaces between the toes on which the bird walks swell up; limping.
Causes: foot injuries caused by sharp-edged stones; in larger birds, perches may not have been properly rounded off or are too small in diameter.
Treatment: clean the birds' feet with soft soap and water; cut open the bunion using a razor blade or scalpel; remove the greasy secretion. Clean with an appropriate tincture (e.g. propolis), ideally using a rubber syringe. Treat the bird in the evening; the following morning, clean with the tincture again and leave the bird in a separate section with clean straw.

In the case of smaller birds, an assistant will be necessary; for larger birds, cover them with a sack, leaving the feet sticking out and keep a firm grip on the bird.

Cannibalism and Foot-Pecking

Symptoms: birds peck at one another's cloaca and feet.
Cause: boredom, too cramped conditions, too few nest boxes, too little straw.
Treatment: remove causes; segregate injured and particularly aggressive birds; cover injured feet with wood tar.

Cholera

See Diarrhoea and Related Diseases

Coccidiosis

See Diarrhoea and Related Diseases

Colds

Head colds, bronchitis, lung infections.
Symptoms: rasping breathing sound, discharge from nose, swollen eyes, exhaustion, diarrhoea.
Causes: damp, cold, draughty housing, damp straw, wetness.
Treatment: remove the causes, use an infra-red lamp, give food with high vitamin content, consult vet.

Comb Scab

Symptoms: mealy deposit on the appendages of the head.
Cause: mould in dirty housing.
Treatment: improve conditions in

which birds are kept; scrub infected places on bird with soft soap and rinse with camomile tea; repeat for several days until the scab or mould can be easily removed.

Crooked Breastbone

Symptoms: the breast is deformed.
Cause: rickets (softening and deformation of bones), sometimes in conjunction with perching in trees at too early an age (before seven weeks – turkeys may start to do this at five weeks). Rickets is the result of a vitamin D deficiency and too little sunlight during rearing.
Treatment: a sunny run, a good supply of greens, calcium (limestone or sterilized egg shell), hard-boiled eggs in the first week (the cholesterol in the yolks will, with sunlight, build up the supply of vitamin D in the skin). Calcium and phosphorus are responsible for the hardening of bones so affected birds should be given milk products in soft food, and bone meal, particularly during rearing. Be careful with vitamin D supplements in food and water because an overdose can also cause disease.

Diarrhoea and Related Diseases

Diarrhoea and diseases involving diarrhoea as a symptom can have many different causes, and are indicated when eggs become soiled with droppings. There are nine of these.

1 Simple diarrhoea
Causes: grit not available for digestion, rotten food, colds due to draughts, wetting and damp straw.
Treatment: remove causes. Medicinal charcoal should be available at all times; give camomile tea instead of water until cured.

2 Bacillary white diarrhoea (BWD) (Pullorum)
Symptoms: white-to-green faeces, white cloaca covered with faeces, cheeping sound during defecation, sores on abdomen, exhaustion, coldness. This condition is now rare in the British Isles.
Cause: infection by salmonella in ovary or contracted during brooding (including brooding performed by an incubator). This does not, however, trigger the disease: it is brought on by extreme temperatures during rearing.
Treatment: clean housing with well-moderated temperatures; keep young birds separate to begin with. Should the disease break out within two days of buying the birds, you may be legally entitled to replacement stock – consult the relevant authority.

3 Blackhead. Occurs in turkeys between 4 and 14 weeks.
Symptoms: white mucus, then yellow diarrhoea, possibly a bluish-copper colour, exhaustion, ruffled feathers, sudden death.
Cause: protozoa infect the liver and caecum; contagious. Chickens may pass on this disease to turkeys without contracting it themselves.
Treatment: given by the vet.
Prevention: not too many birds in the run; keep chickens and turkeys

separate; a run should not be used for young turkeys until one year after it has been vacated by other older turkeys or by chickens. It is possible to administer preventive drugs in the birds' food and water.

4 Cholera. This is a notifiable disease! Sometimes also occurs in water fowl.

Symptoms of an acute attack: watery/flaky diarrhoea, yellow-grey, containing some blood, exhaustion, breathlessness, a blue comb in the case of hens and turkey hens, a blue bill in the case of water fowl, death within a few hours.

Symptoms of cholera: chronic breathlessness and swelling of the joints.

Symptoms of lobe disease (unnotifiable form of cholera): festering throat lobes.

Causes: drinking water contaminated with cholera-type micro-organisms.

Treatment: diseased birds should be killed and burned.

Prevention: clean water, clean housing, good ground cover in run.

5 Coccidiosis. There are two forms of this disease:

(a) Coccidiosis of the caecum

Symptoms: occurs up to eight weeks of age. In chickens, yellowish-brown, later blood-stained diarrhoea, exhaustion, no appetite or thirst, sudden death or slow recovery after six days.

(b) Coccidiosis of the small intestine

Symptoms: occurs after eight weeks of age, but seldom in geese and only very rarely in ducks. In chickens: see above, but the diarrhoea is foamy and yellow in colour. In turkeys: no significant diarrhoea, but weight loss, disrupted growth, death.

Causes: different types of protozoa live in the intestine; their eggs (*oocytes*) are eliminated with the faeces, but they can survive for up to one year in a damp, warm environment. After a few days, the capsules of these oocytes burst open and parasites – now multiplied – are picked up by the bird via the beak.

Treatment: sulphonamide drugs obtainable from the vet; thorough cleaning of the housing; replacement of the straw every 3rd day for two weeks. Use a different run (leave the old run unused for a year). Give nutritious food that is rich in vitamins. Birds which survive this disease will, for a time, be very susceptible to other fatal diseases, so great care should be taken with their living conditions.

Regular administration of coccidiostats (anti-coccidiosis drugs containing low doses of sulphonamide) in the birds' food and water will have no effect if they are not kept in the proper conditions; whereas, if the birds are kept correctly, such drugs are not necessary. In addition, the birds will have, by now, built up an immunity to sulphonamide due to the continuous low dosage, and in serious cases, these drugs – even if administered by the vet in large doses – will be of no effect. Moreover, there is the possibility that the intestines' defence mechanisms will be weakened through the use of these drugs.

6 Fowl pest. This is a notifiable disease!

(a) Classic fowl pest: very rare.

(b) Atypical fowl pest, or Newcastle disease.

Symptoms: green faeces, thirst, exhaustion, discharge from nose, twisting of the neck, gasping.

Cause: virus infection.

Treatment: preventive vaccination of all stock at 1 day old by the vet.

7 Fowl typhoid and paratyphoid. These are notifiable diseases since they may be passed on to humans and to other domestic animals.

Symptoms of typhoid: diarrhoea, loss of weight, discolouring of the comb.

Symptoms of paratyphoid: similar to pullorum. In ducks and geese there will also be thirst, twisting or turning of the head and lameness.

Cause: salmonella resulting from dirty conditions and insufficient sunlight.

Treatment: affected birds must be killed, although in the case of paratyphoid, drugs supplied by the vet may help.

8 Tuberculosis. This is a rare but notifiable disease as it may be passed on to humans and animals.

Symptoms: similar to typhoid. After slaughter, the liver, spleen and intestines exhibit hazelnut-sized yellow spots.

Cause: tubercular bacilli, dirty conditions, too little sunlight, insufficient variety in diet, overcrowded run, old birds.

Treatment: all birds must be killed. The housing and run must not be used for one year; the housing must also be disinfected. The tubercular bacillus can survive temperatures of up to 70°C (158°F), but it cannot take direct sunlight.

9 Worms

Symptoms of threadworms, intestinal worms, tapeworms: diarrhoea, soiled cloaca feathers, ruffled feathers, disturbed growth rate, loss of weight, exhaustion, pallor.

Cause: all young animals, and even humans, are susceptible to worms. With time, immunity will develop naturally, but damp, dirty straw and an overcrowded run are the ideal breeding ground for these parasites.

Treatment: drugs obtainable from the vet; they have the side-effect of making the birds very weak, however. Prevention by means of garlic and onion in the drinking water, as well as grated carrot.

Symptoms of gape worms: coughing, breathlessness.

Cause: worms have infested the trachea and bronchi.

Treatment: drugs obtainable from vet.

Symptoms of gizzard worm: occurs in young geese between 4 and 8 weeks; choking and lameness, death.

Cause: worm infestation of the gut due to dirty conditions.

Treatment: segregate at once, call vet. Provide plenty of clean, dry straw.

Egg-eating

Cause: lack of calcium in diet, or broken eggs resulting from insufficient new straw.

Treatment: remove causes.

Eggs, soft

Symptoms: eggs laid without or with only partial shell covering, soiled abdomen and cloaca feathers.
Causes: calcium or water deficiency, excessive egg production or salpingitis (disease of the oviduct caused by salmonella, bacteria or worms).
Treatment: oystershell, water, an enforced rest from laying by means of a low-protein diet until recovery takes place. In the case of salpingitis, this is not usually possible and the birds will have to be killed.

Eggs, unusual

Double yolks, deformed eggs, extra-large eggs, no yolks, egg within an egg, etc. Occurs occasionally, but in most cases is not related to a disease.

Eye Infection

Symptoms: red, sticky eyes; swollen lids.
Cause: draughts, colds. In the case of young ducks and geese, the water containers may not be deep enough for the birds to dip their whole heads into the water.
Treatment: remove the causes; bathe the eyes several times with lukewarm camomile or eyebright tea (continental European herbal remedy).

Feather Eating

Symptoms: loss of feathers around the cloaca, rump and abdomen, frayed feathers.
Causes: in turkeys, soiled feathers, or boredom, poor ventilation, stress from cramped conditions, glaring light.
Treatment: remove causes.

Fleas

See Vermin

Foot Deformity

Causes: in chickens, incorrect brooding or feeding (*see* 'Crooked Breastbone'); in older birds, may be due to being kept in cage.
Treatment: give chicks food rich in vitamin D, calcium and phosphorus (*see* 'Crooked Breastbone'), and give older birds access to a run. If the symptoms do not improve within a week or two and the birds are prevented from walking, they will need to be killed.

Foot-pecking

See Cannibalism and Foot-pecking

Fowl Pest

See Diarrhoea and Related Diseases

Fowl Typhoid and Paratyphoid

See Diarrhoea and Related Diseases

Laying Difficulties

Symptoms: young chickens in particular may experience difficulty in laying eggs.
Cause: eggs are too large, disease of the ovary.
Treatment: lubricate the cloaca.

Carefully puncture the egg, break it and remove. If this happens repeatedly with a particular bird, it should be put down since it is quite likely to have an incurable disease of the ovary.

Leukosis

Symptoms: loss of weight, pallor, poor laying output.
Cause: viral disease of the liver.
Treatment: affected birds will need to be killed but you must take steps to protect the rest of the flock.

Lice

See Vermin

Lung Inflammation

See Colds

Marek's Disease

Symptoms: limping, wings hanging down; birds die with one leg stretched forwards and the other backwards.
Cause: virus which attacks the bird's brain and nerves.
Prevention: Vaccination of the chicks when one day old, before they are sold. From Week 16, chickens no longer contract this disease, so chicks which have not been immunized should be kept apart from the older birds until that time.

Mites

See Vermin

Moulting

The annual replacement of feathers is a normal and important process. Exceptions to this are the neck moult or exhaustion moult in young chickens that have been fed with protein food too soon.

Turkeys held too long in the hands for some type of treatment will lose their feathers at those points.

Obstruction of the Crop

Symptoms: a bulging crop.
Cause: foreign bodies.
Treatment: have the vet make an incision in the crop, or put the bird down.

Paratyphoid

See Diarrhoea and Related Diseases

Pullorum

See Diarrhoea and Related Diseases

Rickets

See Crooked Breastbone

Salpingitis

See Eggs, soft

Ticks

See Vermin

Tuberculosis

See Diarrhoea and Related Diseases

Typhoid

See Diarrhoea and Related Diseases

Vermin

1 *Lice*
Symptoms: rough, holed feathers; small eggs; 1-3 mm, brown parasites in the cloaca, head and abdomen feathers as well as under the wings; decline in egg-laying activity.
Cause: insufficient opportunity for dust-bath and no wood ash; dirty housing.
Treatment: remove causes, dust with insect powder obtained from the vet. Remember the underneath side of perches when cleaning the housing.

Dusting the feathers with insecticide to control mites and fleas. The natural way is dust bathing, and some people try to enhance this by mixing wood ash with the dust, in the hope of avoiding the use of chemical insecticides

Two poultry parasites: the red mite (left) and the hen flea (right)

2 *Fleas*
Symptoms: restlessness, continuous preening.
Cause and treatment: as for mites.

3 *Mites*
(a) Scaly leg mites. Symptoms: thick crust on the legs and feet; contagious. Cause: dirty quarters. Treatment: remove causes, remembering to clean underneath perches. Treat with soft soap as in comb scab.
(b) Fowl mites. Symptoms: feathers fall out or lack lustre; loss of weight, pale combs; poor laying activity. Cause: see above. Treatment: thorough cleaning of housing. Use a blow lamp on the underneath side of perches; dust with insect powder obtained from the vet. Ensure that the waiting time with respect to the eggs is observed!

4 *Ticks*
Symptoms, cause and treatment: as for fowl mites.

Worms

See Diarrhoea and Related Diseases

PRODUCE FROM YOUR POULTRY

Killing animals and birds is no pleasant task, particularly if you are doing it for the first time, and it amounts to quite a psychological hurdle. However, if you are concerned to have organically produced food, you will still probably prefer to take on the responsibility of rearing and killing the stock yourself, rather than buying a mass-produced bird from a supermarket where it is difficult to find out how the bird was kept or killed.

Killing

The best idea for the beginner is to enlist the help of an experienced neighbour for the first time round. There are also numerous courses in poultry management in colleges and the like, and on these you will certainly see the task demonstrated.

Step by step, the procedure is as follows:

1   In the case of geese and ducks, ensure that on the day before slaughter the birds have plenty of water for the purpose of cleaning their feathers. In the evening, see that they have clean straw so that their feathers remain clean.

2   It is best not to give the birds anything to eat in the last 24 hours. For grazing birds, this means keeping them shut in their housing.

3   The night before slaughter, black out the windows with sacks or boards so that the birds will be in a sleepy state the next morning, and less likely to panic.

4   Ducks and geese will pine for a lost companion, so it is important to slaughter them in pairs or groups as appropriate.

5   See that breeding stock is ringed in advance, so it is impossible for these birds to be killed by mistake.

6   When taking birds out of the pen for slaughter, do so preferably in the dark and use slow, calm movements and a soothing voice. Do everything you can to avoid panic, for birds taken out in an axious state are hard to bleed and even harder to gut. The quality of the meat is affected, too.

7   Take the birds out of the pen one at a time, and carry out the slaughter out of sight of the rest of your stock. The method most commonly used in Britain and many other countries is to dislocate the neck. In other countries the bird is stunned with a blow from a club and then decapitated.

The actual grip for dislocating the neck is best learnt personally from an experienced poultry-keeper, but in brief: hold the bird by the legs in your left hand, breast downwards, at waist level. Grasp the bird's head in your right hand, between first and second fingers. Hold your thumb under the throat.

Stretch the neck downwards, bendng the head forwards until the spinal column is broken, and death is quick and clean.

The correct grip with which to kill a chicken by dislocating its neck: death is quick and clean. In Germany and many other countries, stunning and decapitation are the accepted methods of killing

Some agricultural suppliers may stock a special piece of equipment to do the job for you: this is called a humane killer, and its cost may become financially acceptable if you have a large number of birds to slaughter.

Working with Feathers

Do not attempt too much the first time – one goose or duck will be enough. The whole process – including killing and gutting – can take a good two hours. Do not pluck birds in the house – even if it is a chicken, which tends to have far fewer feathers than a duck or goose.

Preparation

You will need an old chair, three baskets, a rubber apron, some form of head wear and old clothing. Protective clothing is necessary because you will end up looking like a snowman with all the down from the bird clinging to you. Plucking should be done ideally out of doors on a still, sunny day, or in a well-lit shed or barn. Birds should be plucked as soon as they have been killed. The more the body has cooled down, the harder the work will be.

Making Plucking Easier

If you do not intend to make use of duck or goose feathers, you can dip the unplucked body in hot water, which will make plucking a lot easier. Chicken feathers are rarely used in pillows or cushions so they too can be 'dunked', but even if you do not do this, it is not difficult to pluck chickens.

Geese or ducks whose feathers are going to be used may be cleaned by holding them for a short while in hot steam; or you can wrap them in a damp cloth and then apply an iron to this, to produce steam. Make sure that you do not squash the abdomen!

However, since both techniques will cause the feathers to become quite wet, I would not recommend these measures because it can take some time for the feathers to dry, and they may begin to rot in the meanwhile.

If they are to be cleaned later, however, the wet feathers should be put loosely into cotton or linen bags and dried in an oven at a temperature between 50° and 100°C (125-215°F), shaking them and turning them at frequent intervals.

The bird can be held in the lap for plucking or it can be hung up by the feet (using cord or a meat hook).

Plucking

The larger feathers are removed first. They are pulled against the direction in which they have grown because these feathers are very firmly fixed. The next parts to be plucked are those that will cool down most quickly – the wings, legs, neck and rump.

All the different sizes of feathers are put in separate baskets; this must be done as they are plucked so that you end up with all the feathers sorted when you finish plucking. Next come the medium-sized feathers, which are usually clean and have comparatively long (though thin), soft quills. The third basket is used for the downy feathers.

It takes quite a while to pluck a goose or duck completely clean, and it requires a great deal of finger strength. Particular care should be taken when plucking the breast feathers because if too large a clump of downy feathers is pulled out, pieces of skin and meat will often come off with it. This must be put straight on the compost heap because the organic material will go off very quickly. It is best to stretch the skin with your fingers and pull the feathers out in the direction in which they have grown. The younger the bird, the more easily the skin can tear.

Removing the Remaining Down

Once a bird has been plucked as clean as possible by hand, there will still be some down left on it, especially under the wing. There are two possible ways of removing this. You can train a blow-lamp on the bird, keeping well back so only the heat (and not the flame) touches the skin; you must exercise great care when doing this.

Alternatively, you can dip the bird into liquid wax. Special wax for this purpose can be obtained from poultry-keeping suppliers; it is not cheap, but it is very useful. The bird is then immersed in cold water and may be put into a refrigerator for a while. Finally the wax coating, which will now have set, can be removed together with all the residual feathers. Remember to remove the wax in the direction of growth of the feathers. The used wax can then be melted down and used again.

Making Pillows and Feather beds

In most cases, the feathers obtained will find their way into your own pillows or cushions. After they have been plucked, the down and downy feathers are put into an old pillow-slip which is hung up to air and dry. Every now and then they should be carefully shaken. They will then be ready for use the following autumn.

It is best to have them cleaned once more at a specialist feather-bed making workshop, but they should not be 'eulanized' (dry cleaned) because poisonous substances are often used

To avoid feathers flying all over the house, it is best to pluck birds outside

for this and you do not really want these substances in your bed!

Preparing Birds for the Table

To gut birds, you will need a large, clean table-top with good lighting, a small, sharp-pointed kitchen knife, a somewhat larger knife, a plate and a bowl. The bowl is for parts destined for the compost heap; the plate is for parts kept for use in the kitchen.

With the large knife, the feet are cut off at the joint (i.e. where the leathery skin ends); these will go into the bowl for the compost heap. The neck, with its skin, is severed at the shoulder.

It was the practice to make an incision in the skin of the neck and remove the trachea (windpipe), oesophagus (gullet) and crop, but since the whole neck is invariably removed these days, this procedure is no longer necessary. The skin of the neck is taken off and with it the crop, trachea and oesophagus (cats will find these a great delicacy). Put the skinned neck on the plate.

The bird should now be turned onto its back. Place the small kitchen knife beneath the breast bone and carefully make a not-too-deep cut as far as the cloaca. The abdominal cavity can now be opened. Take hold of the end of the intestines, cut away the membranes holding the cloaca (ensuring that no faeces are dislodged to spoil the meat) and pull the intestines out with the cloaca. Put these into the compost-heap bowl.

Now insert the fingers into the abdominal cavity and loosen the thin internal membranes. Take hold of as much of the entrails as possible and carefully pull them out. Carefully cut the liver away from the gall bladder: the liver goes on to the plate and the gall bladder into the bowl. The stomach is cut at the narrow end and emptied, and the whitish-yellow inner skin is removed; the older the bird, the harder this will be to remove. Put the stomach on the plate. The heart is then taken out through the abdominal cavity; its glassy covering and arteries are removed, and the remaining heart muscle is put on the plate.

Finally, the remains of the lungs, cartilage, trachea and oesophagus and the testicles or ovary are removed and discarded. The bird can now be thoroughly rinsed with cold running water.

In the legs of turkeys, there are six tendons which will have to be removed using pliars. Since they are very sharp edged, you should not pull them out by hand. If these tendons are not removed, the legs will become so hard when they are cooked that there will be no enjoyment in eating them.

If you have a cool, dry room available, the birds can now be hung, with the neck opening upwards for two to three days. If not, the bird can be used at once or it can be frozen.

Moulting and its Effects on the Table-ready Bird

When chicks hatch, their downy feathers are still enclosd in horny sheaths which very quickly burst open and fall off in fine particles known as 'chick dust'. In the same layer, known as the *papilla*, from which the downy feathers grow, there are also the real feathers which will replace them. Depending on the inherited growth rate, the development of feathers can be observed a few hours after hatching, the first ones appearing on the rump and on the wings.

The moulting process is controlled by hormones from the thyroid gland, which is also connected with the development of the sexual organs. Females lay no eggs at this time, males refrain from courting behaviour and, as an outward sign, the combs shrink. Since moulting requires a great deal of strength and energy, it is only natural that egg production falls at this time. However, after this period of regeneration,

the birds resume laying vigorously.

During the moulting period, new feathers form in the papilla and push out the old feathers they are to replace. Young feathers continue to grow for a while and therefore have food carried to their bases in the blood; that is why blood is visible if an unripe feather is plucked. The feather shafts remain in the skin when the feathers are plucked out; the skin is covered by a large number of these small holes. It is only possible to remove the shafts by the painstaking use of tweezers.

If at all possible, you should arrange things so that birds are not on the point of moulting when they are slaughtered. Otherwise, the skin will be covered with fine stubble. Chickens and turkeys moult mostly in autumn, but ducks and geese moult at different times, depending on their age. With ducks and geese, first the tail and small outer feathers fall out, then the pinions. When the run is strewn with feathers and the average-sized tail feathers are coming out, this marks the start of moulting, which will last for three weeks.

Ducks moult at about the age of ten weeks, and Pekin ducks every eight to ten weeks thereafter. If they already weigh 2 to 2.5 kg (4½-5½ lb) at this point, they should be killed before they moult. After moulting has started, it will be necessary to wait another seven weeks until the birds are able to be plucked. Geese moult for the first time when they are around 12 weeks old. Thereafter you must wait seven weeks after the start of every moult for the feathers to be ready for plucking.

SUPPLIERS AND INFORMATION

Sources of supply of stock, housing, equipment and feed are best located through advertisements in local newspapers and in specialist poultry and farming magazines. We give here a brief world-wide selection from the literature available giving advice on specialist and general poultry-keeping topics, and directing readers to local organizations and suppliers.

Australia

The Poultry Farmer

Canada

Canada Poultryman
The Western Producer

France

L'Aviculteur

Germany, Federal Republic

Deutsche Geflügelwirtschaft

Ireland

Irish Farmer's Journal

India

Poultry Pen
Poultry Punch

Netherlands

Pluimvee Houderig
Poultry (in English)

South Africa

Pluimvee/Poultry (in English and Afrikaans)

United Kingdom

Fancy Fowl
Farmer's Guardian
Farmer's Weekly
Home Farm
Poultry Forum
Poultry International★
Poultry World
The Scottish Farmer
The Smallholder
Turkeys
World Poultry★
World Poultry Science Journal

USA

Poultry Digest
Poultry Times
Poultry Tribune
Turkey World

International Organization

The main world body for poultry-keeping is the World's Poultry Science Association, with branches in 40 countries. Its secretary is Frau Dr Rose-Marie Wegner, Institut für Kleintierzucht, 3100 Celle, Dornbergstrasse 25/27, Federal Republic of Germany.

★Publishes an annual world directory of suppliers and poultry organizations.

GENERAL CHARACTERISTICS OF POULTRY SPECIES

	Chickens	Turkeys	Ducks	Geese
Wholly vegetarian				×
Grazing birds	×	×	×	××
Insectivores	×	×	×	
Water birds			××	×
Flyers	×○	×○	○×	○×
			Flying Ducks ××	
Run should offer good visibility		×	×	××
Good ground cover required	××	×	×	
Well-insulated housing needed	×			
Strict pecking order	×	○×		
Strong family ties				×
Loose relations			×	
Produces down			×	×
Edible eggs	×	×	×	×
Good brooding characteristics	×○	××	○	○×

× = yes, ○ = limited

138

SPACE REQUIREMENTS

	Housing	Run
Chicken	0.5 sq m (5.3 sq ft)	20 sq m (214 sq ft)
Turkey	1.0 sq m (11 sq ft)	30-50 sq m (321-530 sq ft)
Duck	0.5 sq m (5.3 sq ft)	30-50 sq m (321-530 sq ft) + water
Goose	0.5 sq m (5.3 sq ft)	125-200 sq m (1340-2140 sq ft + water
10 hens + cockerel	6.0 sq m (65 sq ft) + fittings	150-200 sq m (1600-2140 sq ft)
1 broody + 10 chicks	5.0 sq m (53 sq ft) + fittings	50-100 sq m (530-1070 sq ft) according to age
Pair of turkeys + offspring	12.0 sq m (130 sq ft)	350 sq m (3750 sq ft)
Pair of ducks + offspring	9.0 sq m (96 sq ft)	400 sq m (4300 sq ft) + water
Pair of geese + offspring	9.0 sq m (96 sq ft)	1000-1500 sq m (10,700-16,000 sq ft) + water

REPRODUCTION (northern hemisphere)

	Chickens	Turkeys
Laying period	all year (except during moulting, brooding and rearing)	February–April
Possibly broody	April–October	March–May
Best brooding time	April	April
Duration of brooding (days)	21	28
Number of eggs per brood	up to 15	up to 15
Ratio of males to females	1:10-20	1:8-15
Best age for reproduction, as from:	Male: 12 months Female: 24 months	Male: 8 months Female: 8 months

EGG AND MEAT YIELDS

	Chickens	Turkeys
Eggs/year	150-260	60-180
Egg weight	50-65 g (1¾-2¼ oz)	70-90 g (2¼-3 oz)
Ready for laying	25-28 weeks	200-250 days
Feeding/fattening period	Cockerels and pullets 10-15 weeks	20-25 weeks
Weight when killed	from 1.5 kg (3¼ lb)	6-18 kg (13-40 lb)
Moulting	Autumn	Autumn

	Ducks		Geese
	Muscovy ducks	**All other ducks**	
	Spring Summer Autumn	January–July (Indian Runner: autumn–spring)	February–May
	2-3 times a year	Mainly in spring, but also later	February–May
	April	April & later	April
	35	24–28	28-32
	up to 15	up to 15	up to 15
	1:1	1:3-4	1:3-4 (Toulouse goose 1:1)
	As for all other ducks	Male: 7-8 months Female: 7-8 months	Male & Female: 1 year and older (Toulouse goose: 2 years and older)

EGG AND MEAT YIELDS

Ducks	Geese
100-250	30-80
70-80 g (2¼-2½ oz)	170-200 g (6-7 oz)
28 weeks	280-300 days
9-10 weeks	11-12 weeks if sold as young geese, or 7-8 months if sold as Christmas geese
2-5 kg (4½-11 lb)	4-15 kg (9-33 lb)
About 10 weeks after hatching; 2 partial moults at 3-week intervals; Pekin ducks every 8-10 weeks	About 12-13 weeks after hatching; 2 partial moults at 3-week intervals

INDEX

Page numbers in **bold type** refer to pictures